MCAT

General Chemistry
Review Notes

© 2009 by Kaplan, Inc.

Published by Kaplan Publishing, a division of Kaplan, Inc.
1 Liberty Plaza, 24th Floor
New York, NY 10006

In partnership with Kaplan's National MCAT Team, 1440 Broadway, 8th Floor, New York, NY 10018.

Printed in the United States of America

10 9 8 7 6 5 4 3 2 1

ISBN: 978-1-60714-439-7

Kaplan Publishing books are available at special quantity discounts to use for sales promotions, employee premiums, or educational purposes. Please email our Special Sales Department to order or for more information at kaplanpublishing@kaplan.com, or write to Kaplan Publishing, 1 Liberty Plaza, 24th Floor, New York, NY 10006.

Planet Friendly Publishing
✔ Made in the United States
✔ Printed on Recycled Paper
GREEN EDITION
Learn more at www.greenedition.org

• Manufacturing books in the United States ensures compliance with strict environmental laws and eliminates the need for international freight shipping, a major contributor to global air pollution. Printing on recycled paper helps minimize our consumption of trees, water and fossil fuels.
• Trees Saved: 103 • Air Emissions Eliminated: 10,329 pounds
• Water Saved: 37,471 gallons • Solid Waste Eliminated: 5,551 pounds

Contributors

The Kaplan MCAT Review Notes Series was created by a dedicated team of 45 professionals who worked a combined total of over 11,000 hours.

This text would not exist without the tireless work of Cait Clancy, Henry Conant, Ed Crawford, PhD, Suneetha Desiraju, Marilyn Engle, Christopher Falzone, PhD, Sheryl Gordon, Walter Hartwig, PhD, Jeannie Ho, Jessica Kim, Jeff Koetje, MD, John Linick, Keith Lubeley, Amjed Mustafa, Joanna Myllo, Glen Pearlstein, MD, Dominique Polfliet, Ira Rothstein, PhD, Matthew Wilkinson, and Sze Yan.

Special thanks to: Jesse Barrett, Susan E. Barry, Geri Burgert, Deana Casamento, Robin Garmise, Rita Garthaffner, Chip Hurlburt, Colette Mazunik, Danielle Mazza, Stephanie McCann, Diane McGarvey, Maureen McMahon, Jason Miller, Jason Moss, Maria Nicholas, Walt Niedner, Jeff Olson, Rochelle Rothstein, MD, Lisa Pallatroni, John Polstein, Ron Sharpe, Brian Shorter, Glen Stohr, Martha Torres, Bob Verini, and the countless others who made this project possible.

Using This Book

This book is designed to help you review the science topics covered on the MCAT. It represents one of the content review resources available to you in the Kaplan program. Additional review is available through the live and on-demand lessons, the library of available practice tests and explanations-on-demand that accompany them, and your flashcards and QuickSheets.

Please understand that content review, no matter how thorough, is not sufficient preparation for the MCAT! The MCAT Biological Sciences and Physical Sciences sections test your reading, reasoning, and problem-solving skills, as well as your science knowledge. Don't assume that simply memorizing the contents of this book will earn you high science scores—it won't. If you want your best shot at great science scores, you must also improve your reading and test-taking skills through the lessons, testing sessions, and the Kaplan and AAMC practice tests in the Training Library. So resist the temptation to reread this book at the expense of taking practice tests! Rather, strike a balance between content review and critical reasoning practice.

At the end of each chapter, you'll find MCAT-style review questions and open-ended questions for study group discussion. These are designed to help you assess your understanding of the chapter you just read.

The last chapter of this book is a special section devoted to what we call the High-Yield Problem Solving Guide. Although not presented exactly in the style of the MCAT, these questions tackle the most frequently tested topics found on the test. For each type of problem, the guide will provide you with a stepwise technique for solving the question and key directional points on how to solve specifically for the MCAT.

Consult the Syllabus in your MCAT Lesson Book for specific reading/practice assignments. Reading the appropriate chapters will greatly enhance your understanding of the lesson material. A glossary and index are included in the back of each review book for easy reference.

This is your book, so write in the margin, highlight the key points—do whatever is necessary to help you get that higher score. It should be your trusty companion as Test Day approaches.

Sincerely,
The Kaplan MCAT Team

About Scientific American

As the world's premier science and technology magazine, and the oldest continuously published magazine in the United States, Scientific American is committed to bringing the most important developments in modern science, medicine, and technology to 3.5 million readers worldwide in an understandable, credible and provocative format.

Founded in 1845 and on the "cutting edge" ever since, Scientific American boasts over 140 Nobel laureate authors including Albert Einstein, Francis Crick, Stanley Prusiner and Richard Axel. Scientific American is a forum where scientific theories and discoveries are explained to a broader audience.

Scientific American published its first foreign edition in 1890, and in 1979, was the first Western magazine published in the People's Republic of China. Today, Scientific American is published in 17 foreign language editions with a total circulation of more than 1 million worldwide. Scientific American is also a leading online destination (www.ScientificAmerican.com), providing the latest science news and exclusive features to more than 2 million unique visitors monthly.

The knowledge that fills our pages has the power to inspire, spark new ideas, paradigms and visions for the future. As science races forward, Scientific American continues to cover the promising strides, inevitable setbacks and challenges, and new medical discoveries as they unfold.

Guide To Margin Notes:

Our Review Notes are designed with ample white space for you to take notes while you work your way through the Kaplan MCAT program. Periodically, you'll come across some of our own comments in the margins. We call these sidebars "margin notes" (pretty clever, right?).

The following is a legend of the five main types of margin notes you'll find in the science Review Notes:

Real World: These notes are designed to illustrate how a concept discussed in the text relates to the practice of medicine and the world at large. Since you are a premed (if not, you're reading the wrong book), we felt that these correlations would both be of interest to you and help solidify your understanding of some key concepts.

Key Concept: These are synopses of the concepts discussed on a page. Typically, we reserved this type of margin note for pages where lots of important and complex information was presented.

Bridge: We use "Bridges" to alert you to the conceptual links that occur between chapters or disciplines.

MCAT Expertise: These are designed to illuminate some of the conceptual patterns that the testmaker tends to focus on when writing MCAT questions.

Mnemonics: Sometimes they rhyme, and sometimes they don't. But we hope that they will all help you recall information quickly on Test Day.

Contents

Atomic Structure

"Salting the water makes the pasta cook faster because the salt raises the boiling point. It's chemistry—it's a colligative property." My colleague sat smugly and stared me down, as if the intensity of his gaze gave further credence to his pronouncement. It was late on a Friday afternoon, about 5:00 P.M.—and the science of cooking had become the topic of discussion that would carry us through the final hour of the workweek. If ours were a more typical office, we might have been discussing our weekend plans involving the consumption of legal liquid intoxicants. As employees of an educational company, we might have been forgiven for discussing the biochemical basis of intoxication. However, here we were, arguing over the relative merits of culinary and scientific justifications for adding salt to pasta water. We were two opposing camps: one side arguing that adding salt to the water served no real purpose other than to flavor the pasta as it absorbed the water; and the other side—the one of my colleague and his compatriots—fighting in the name of science. Finally, we agreed on a plan toward resolution and a lasting peace. We would calculate the actual chemical impact of the salt in the water and answer the question *Why add salt to pasta water?* once and for all.

Well, you can figure out the details of the calculation if you are so inclined, but suffice it to say that I wouldn't be telling you this story if I hadn't been proven correct. Our calculation showed that the amount of salt that most of us would probably consider a reasonably sufficient quantity for a large pot of boiling water had minimal impact on the boiling point temperature of the resulting solution. To be clear, the addition of the salt did raise the boiling point temperature—and even those of us arguing against the "scientific justification" never denied that it would. Nevertheless, the calculated rise in boiling point was exceedingly small, because the solution we imagined had such a low molality. The truth of the matter is this: adding salt to cooking water in reasonable amounts does not measurably increase the boiling point temperature or decrease the cooking time. The salt merely flavors the food as it cooks in the dilute solution.

Why introduce a book of general chemistry for the MCAT review by telling you a story about food preparation? Am I telling you this simply to showcase an instance in which I won an argument? No, it's because chemistry is the study of the stuff of life or, to put it more properly, the nature and behavior of matter. Chemistry is the investigation of the atoms and molecules that make up our bodies, our possessions, the world around us, and of course, the food that we eat. There are different branches of chemistry, two of which are tested directly on the MCAT—general inorganic chemistry and organic chemistry—but ultimately all investigations in the realm of chemistry are seeking to answer the questions that confront us in the form (literally, "form": the shape, structure, mode, and essence) of the physical world that surrounds us.

At this point, you're probably saying the same thing you say when talking about physics: *But I'm premed, why do I need to know any of this? What good will this do me as a doctor? Do I only need to know this for the MCAT?* Let me make it clearer for you: *How can you expect to be an effective doctor for your patients—who are made of the organic and inorganic stuff—unless you understand how this stuff makes up and affects the human body?*

So, let's get down to the business of learning and remembering the principles of the physical world that help us understand what all this stuff is, and how it works, and why it behaves the way it does, at both the molecular and macroscopic levels. In the process of reading through these chapters and applying your knowledge to practice questions, you'll prepare yourself for success not only on the Physical Science section of the MCAT but also in the medical care of your patients and the larger communities you will serve as a trained physician.

This first chapter starts our review of general chemistry with a consideration of the fundamental unit of matter, the atom, and the even smaller particles that constitute the atom: protons, neutrons, and electrons. We will also review the two models of the atom with a particular focus on how the two models are similar and different.

Subatomic Particles

Although you may have encountered in your university-level chemistry classes such subatomic particles as quarks, leptons, gluons and other particles whose names sound as if they were picked up from a *Star Trek* episode, the MCAT's approach to atomic structure is much simpler. There are three subatomic particles that you must understand.

MCAT Expertise

The building blocks of the atom are also the building blocks of knowledge for the General Chemistry concepts tested on the MCAT. By understanding these interactions, we will be able to use that as the "nucleus" of understanding to all of General Chemistry.

SUBSTANCE ATOM NUCLEUS

Figure 1.1

PROTONS

Protons are found, along with neutrons, in the nucleus of an atom. Each proton has an amount of charge equal to the fundamental unit of charge (1.6×10^{-19} C) and we frequencies and is thus known as a *line spectrum,* where each line on the emission spectrum corresponds to a specific electronic transition. Because each element can have its electrons excited to different distinct energy levels, each one possesses a unique atomic emission spectrum, which can be used as a fingerprint for the element. One particular application of atomic emission spectroscopy is in the analysis of stars and planets: while a physical sample may be impossible to procure, the light from a star can be resolved into its component wavelengths, which are then matched to the known line spectra of the elements.

The Bohr model of the hydrogen atom explained the atomic emission spectrum of hydrogen, which is the simplest emission spectrum among all the elements. The group of hydrogen emission lines corresponding to transitions from the upper energy levels $n > 2$ to $n = 2$ (that is to say, the pattern of photon emissions from the electron falling from the $n > 2$ energy level to the $n = 2$ energy level) is known as the *Balmer series* and includes four wavelengths in the visible region. The group corresponding to transitions from the upper levels $n > 1$ to $n = 1$ (that is to say, the emissions of photons from the electron falling from the higher energy levels to the ground state) is called the *Lyman series,* which include larger energy transitions and therefore shorter photon wavelengths, in the UV region of the electromagnetic spectrum.

> **Real World**
>
> Emissions from electrons in molecules, or atoms dropping from an excited state to a ground state, give rise to fluorescence. We see the color of the emitted light.

When the energy of each frequency of light observed in the emission spectrum of hydrogen was calculated according to Planck's quantum theory, the values obtained closely matched those expected from energy level transitions in the Bohr model. That is, the energy associated with a change in the quantum number from an initial higher value n_i to a final lower value n_f is equal to the energy of the photon predicted by Planck's quantum theory. Combining Bohr's and Planck's calculations, we arrive at:

$$E = \frac{hc}{\lambda} = -R_H \left[\frac{1}{n_i^2} - \frac{1}{n_f^2} \right]$$

The energy of the emitted photon corresponds to the precise difference in energy between the higher-energy initial state and the lower-energy final state.

Atomic Absorption Spectra

When an electron is excited to a higher energy level, it must absorb energy. The energy absorbed that enables an electron to jump from a lower-energy level to a higher one is characteristic of that transition. This means that the excitation of electrons in the atoms of a particular element results in energy absorption at specific wavelengths. Thus, in addition to a unique emission spectrum, every element possesses a characteristic absorption spectrum. Not surprisingly, the wavelengths of absorption correspond directly to the wavelengths of emission because the difference in energy between levels remains unchanged. Identification of elements present in a gas phase sample requires absorption spectra.

MCAT Expertise

ΔE is the same for absorption or emission between any two energy levels. The sign (positive or negative) of ΔE indicates whether the energy goes in or out and therefore whether the electron is going to an excited state (absorption) or to the ground state (emission), respectively.

You've just been put through a series of paragraphs crammed with technical language (mumbo jumbo is too strong a term; after all, you are sufficiently intelligent enough to grasp these concepts). That said, at least a few pairs of eyes reading this book will have gone glassy by this point. Therefore, let's bring this back to the realm of experience by way of analogy. We've already discussed equating the energy levels available to electrons to stairs on a staircase. Taking this analogy one step further, so to speak: let's imagine that you and your friend are walking side-by-side up to a set of stairs. You have very long legs and so it is your habit to take two, sometimes even three, steps at a time; your friend has short legs and so takes one, or at most two, steps at a time. The pattern by which you jump from a lower step to a higher one will be characteristic to you and you alone and will be quite different from the pattern by which your friend jumps from a lower step to a higher one, which will be unique to her. Furthermore, you have to invest energy into the process of ascending the staircase. This, in a nutshell is the significance of the atomic absorption spectrum. The atomic emission spectrum is simply a record of the process in reverse.

Quantum Mechanical Model of Atoms

While Bohr's model marked a significant advancement in the understanding of the structure of atoms (at least we were no longer talking about plum pudding), his model ultimately proved inadequate to explain the structure and behavior of atoms containing more than one electron. The model's failure was a result of Bohr's not taking into account the repulsion between multiple electrons surrounding one nucleus. Modern quantum mechanics has led to a more rigorous and generalized study of the electronic structure of atoms. The most important difference between Bohr's model and the modern quantum mechanical model is that Bohr postulated that electrons follow a clearly defined circular pathway or orbit at a fixed distance from the nucleus, whereas modern quantum mechanics has shown that this is not the case. Rather, we now understand that electrons move rapidly in extraordinarily complex patterns within regions of space around the nucleus called **orbitals.** The confidence by which those in Bohr's time believed they could identify the location (or pathway) of the electron is now replaced by a more modest suggestion that the best we can do is describe the probability of finding an electron within a given region of space surrounding the nucleus. In the current quantum mechanical model, it is impossible to pinpoint exactly where an electron is at any given moment in time, and this is expressed best by the **Heisenberg uncertainty principle**: *it is impossible to simultaneously determine, with perfect accuracy, the momentum and the position of an electron*. If we want to assess the position of an electron, the electron has to stop (thereby changing its momentum); if we want to assess its momentum, the electron has to be moving (thereby changing its position).

16. Which of the following statements is NOT true of an electron's ground state?

    A. The electron is at its lowest possible energy level.

    B. The electron is in a quantized energy level.

    C. The electron is traveling along its smallest possible orbital radius.

    D. The electron is static.

17. Which of the following experimental conditions would NOT excite an electron out of the ground state?

    A. Radiation

    B. High temperature

    C. High pressure

    D. None of the above

Small Group Questions

1. Which orbital fills first: $4s$ or $3d$? Which is first to give up electrons?

2. Why do atoms have neutrons? What purpose do they serve?

Explanations to Practice Questions

1. A

Because an electron was pulled off the neutral parent atom, consider how that parent atom was formed and which electron it would be willing to give up. Zn° has 30 electrons, so it would have an electron configuration of $1s^2 2s^2 2p^6 3s^2 3p^6 4s^2 3d^{10}$. Subshells strongly prefer to be completely empty, exactly half-full, or completely full. Therefore, the best way to lose two electrons and form Zn^{2+} is to pull them both out of the 4s-orbital. (B) implies that electrons are pulled out of the d-orbital, (C) presents the configuration of the uncharged zinc atom, and (D) shows the configuration that would exist if four electrons were removed.

2. B

The azimuthal quantum number l, cannot be higher than $n - 1$, ruling out (A). The m_l number, which describes the chemical's magnetic properties, can only be an integer value between $-l$ and l, and cannot be equal to 1 if $l = 0$, ruling out (C) and (D).

3. C

The correct answer is (C), $2n^2$. If you did not know this formula by heart, you can calculate it using your knowledge of the four quantum numbers. For the s-subshell, the principal quantum number is $n = 0$; $n = 1$ for the p-subshell; and $n = 2$ for the d-subshell. (Larger values of n suggest higher energy levels farther from the nucleus of the atom, as you know energy is quantized—that is, it differs by discrete amounts—between shells.)

4. B

This formula describes the number of electrons in terms of the azimuthal quantum number l, which ranges from 0 to $n - 1$, n being the principal quantum number.

Subshell	Azimuthal Quantum Number (l)	Number of Electrons
s	0	2
p	1	6
d	2	10
f	3	14

Using the data in the table, the quickest way to solve this problem is to choose a subshell and plug in its l value to solve for the number of electrons. If more than one option works, discard the others and test the remaining possibilities using another subshell.

5. D

Sulfur is diamagnetic, as opposed to ferromagnetic (iron, cobalt) or paramagnetic (hydrogen). Ferromagnetism refers, loosely, to the ability of a surface to attract an external magnetic field. It is characteristic of iron (Fe), from which it derives its name. More specifically, paramagnetism describes the tendency of valence electrons to align with the same spin in the presence of a strong magnetic field. Strongly paramagnetic materials, including transition metals, are usually called ferromagnetic. Transition metals like iron are characterized by a "sea" of electrons moving freely about the surface, which makes it easier for all these electrons to align in one direction. (This electron "sea" is an imprecise model, but good enough for the MCAT.) It is harder for more stable elements (e.g. oxygen, halogens, noble gases) to align their electrons in one orientation because their orbitals are nearly filled; these substances are known as diamagnetic. Sulfur has a similar atomic structure to oxygen, so it is also diamagnetic.

6. C

The problem requires the MCAT favorite equation $E = hf$, where $h = 6.626 \times 10^{-34}$ (Planck's constant) and f is the frequency of the photon. (Memorize Planck's constant!) One can calculate the frequency of the photon using the provided wavelength, 500 nm, with the equation $f = c/\lambda$, where $c = 3 \times 10^8$ m/s, the speed of light. Here, $f = (3 \times 10^8$ m/s$)/500 \times 10^{-9}$ m, or 6×10^{14} s^{-1} (1 Hz = 1 s^{-1}). That leads to $E = hf$, or $E = (6.626 \times 10^{-34}) \times (6 \times 10^{14}$ Hz$) = 3.98 \times 10^{-19}$ J. (Don't worry about memorizing the units of Planck's constant—energy is always in joules!). However, the problem includes an additional trick, in that the answer must account for a mole of photons. The $E = hf$ equation works for a single photon only. Thus the answer must account for this using Avogadro's number, 6.022×10^{23} photons. Multiply (3.98×10^{-19} J/photon) $\times$ (6.022×10^{23} photons) $= 2.39 \times 10^5$ J.

7. B

There is not enough information in the problem to determine how the velocity of the electron will change. There will be some energy change, however, as the electron must lose energy to return to the minimum energy ground state. That will require emitting radiation in the form of a photon, (B).

8. A

Recall that the superscript (i.e., the A in ^{A}C) refers to the mass number of an electron, which is equal to the number of protons plus the number of neutrons present in an element. (Sometimes a text will list the atomic number, Z, or total number of protons, under the mass number A.) According to the periodic table, carbon contains 6 protons, therefore its atomic number (Z) = 6. An isotope contains the same number of protons and a different number of neutrons as the element. Carbon is most likely to have an atomic number of 12, for 6 protons and 6 neutrons. (C) and (D) are possible isotopes that would have more neutrons than does ^{12}C. The ^{6}C isotope is unlikely. It would mean that there were 6 protons and 0 neutrons, and it would probably collapse under the stress of the positive charge.

9. C

The Heisenberg uncertainty principle states that you cannot know the position and momentum of a particle simultaneously, which eliminates (A) and (D). Momentum depends on velocity (recall from Newtonian mechanics that $p = mv$) so in order to calculate momentum, velocity must be known. (C) explains this.

10. B

In order for the electron to *gain* energy, it must absorb photons to jump up to a higher energy level. This eliminates (A) and (D). Between (B) and (C), there is a bigger jump between $n = 2$ and $n = 6$ than there is between $n = 3$ and $n = 4$. Therefore, (B) represents the greatest energy gain.

11. A

The MCAT covers qualitative topics more often than quantitative topics in this unit. It is critical to be able to distinguish the fundamental principles that determine electron organization, which are usually known by the names of the scientists who discovered them. The Heisenberg uncertainty principle refers to the momentum and position of a single electron, and the Bohr model was an early attempt to describe the behavior of the single electron in a hydrogen atom. (D) is tempting, but (A) is more complete and therefore the correct answer. The element shown here, nitrogen, is often used to demonstrate Hund's rule because it is the smallest element with a half-filled *p*-subshell. Hund's rule explains that electrons fill empty orbitals first, and in fact, the three *p*-electrons in this image each occupy a separate orbital. Hund's rule is really a corollary of the Pauli exclusion principle, in that the Pauli exclusion principle suggests that each orbital contains two electrons of opposite spin. Additional electrons must fill new orbitals so the compound remains stable in its ground state.

12. A

The quickest way to solve this problem is to use the periodic table and find out how many protons are in Cs atoms, which happens to be 55. Neutral Cs atoms would also have 55 electrons. A Cs cation is most likely to have a single positive charge because it has one unpaired *s*-electron. This translates to one fewer electron than the number or protons, or 54 electrons.

13. B

The easiest way to approach this problem is to set up a system of two algebraic equations, where x and y are the percentages of H (mass = 1 amu) and D (mass = 2 amu), respectively. Your setup should look like the following system:

$x + y = 1$ (proportion H (x) + proportion D (y) in whole, $x\% + y\% = 100\%$).

$1x + 2y = 1.008$ (the total atomic mass)

Substitute one variable for the other so the atomic mass is in terms of one variable $(1 - y = x)$, then solve for the other percentage $([1 - y] + 2y = 1.008$; simplifies to $0.008 = y$, or 0.8% D). That plus 99.2 percent H makes 100 percent. Another way to examine this problem is if we had 50 percent of H and 50 percent of D, we could probably imagine an atomic mass of 1.5 amu. Therefore, if 50 percent D gave a mass of 1.5 amu, 80 percent D would yield an atomic mass of 1.8 amu. Eight percent would result in 1.08 amu, and 0.8 percent in 1.008 amu, which is the desired mass.

14. A

The terms in the answer choices refer to the magnetic spin of the two electrons. The quantum number m_s represents this property as a measure of the electrons' relative intrinsic angular momentum. These electrons' spins are parallel, in that their spins are aligned in the same direction $(m_s = +\frac{1}{2}$ for both species). (B), (C), and (D) suppose that $m_s = +\frac{1}{2}$ for one electron and $-\frac{1}{2}$ for the other. (D) implies that the two electrons have opposite spins but lie within the same orbital.

15. B

When dealing with ions, you cannot directly approach electronic configurations based on the number of electrons they currently hold. First examine the neutral atom's configuration, and then determine which electrons would have been removed.

Neutral Atom's Configuration	Ion's Configuration
Cr^0: [Ar] $4s^2 3d^4$	—
Mn^0: [Ar] $4s^2 3d^5$	Mn^+: [Ar] $4s^1 3d^5$
Fe^0: [Ar] $4s^2 3d^6$	Fe^{2+}: [Ar] $4s^0 3d^6$
Co^0: [Ar] $4s^2 3d^7$	Co^{3+}: [Ar] $4s^0 3d^6$

Cr has no electrons removed after filling its orbitals sequentially, which means the $4s$-orbital would have to remain full. Mn must lose one electron from its initial configuration to become the Mn^+ cation. That electron would come from the $4s$-orbital, because the $3d$-orbital would strongly prefer to remain half-full. This d-orbital's desire to be half-full trumps the s-orbital's desire to be completely full, because it is at a higher energy. Fe must lose two electrons to become Fe^{2+}. They'll both be lost from the same orbital, because the scientist can't pick and choose which electrons to take! Moreover, the only way Fe^{2+} could hold the configuration in the question stem would be if one d-electron and one s-electron were lost together. Cobalt would also lose two electrons from the $4s$-orbital first, leaving one to be extracted from $3d$.

16. D

(D) is the only incorrect statement in the set. Electrons are assumed to be in motion in any energy level, even in the ground state. All of the other statements are true. The electron's principal quantum number, or energy level, is $n = 1$. It must be an integer value in the ground state and in the excited state. This number gives a relative indication of the electron's distance from the nucleus, so it must have the smallest radius of all the energy levels. The farther the electron moves from the nucleus, the greater energy it needs to overcome its attractive forces.

17. C

High pressure is unlikely to excite an electron out of the ground state unless it causes an extreme change in temperature, which would add enough energy to the system to promote the electron. There is not enough information in the problem to determine whether the stated high pressure would be high enough, as the answer is too generic. Irradiation has the same effect as temperature.

The Periodic Table

Types of Elements

It's often been said that birds of a feather flock together and this is no less true for the elements. When we consider the trends of chemical reactivity and physical properties taken together, we begin to identify whole clans, if you will, of elements that share sets of similarities. These larger collections of elements span groups and periods, divided into three categories: metals, nonmetals, and metalloids (semimetals).

METALS

Metals are found both on the left side and in the middle of the periodic table, and include the active metals, the transition metals, and the lanthanide and actinide series of elements. Metals are shiny solids, except for mercury, which is a liquid under standard state conditions. They generally have high melting points and densities but there are exceptions, such as lithium, which has a density that is about half that of water. Metals have the ability to be deformed without breaking; the ability of metal to be hammered into shapes is called **malleability** and its ability to be drawn into wires is called **ductility.** At the atomic level, low Z_{eff}, low electronegativity (high electropositivity), large atomic radius, and low ionization energy define metals. These characteristics make it fairly easy for metals to give up one or more electrons. Many of the transition metals, for example, are known to have two oxidation states and some have more than that. Because the valence electrons of all metals are only loosely held to their atoms, they are essentially free to move, which makes metals generally good conductors of heat and electricity (some are better than others). The valence electrons of the active metals are found in the *s*-subshell, those of the transition metals are found in the *d*-subshell, and those of the lanthanide and actinide series elements are found in the *f*-subshell. Some transition metals—such as copper, nickel, silver, gold, palladium, and platinum—are relatively nonreactive, a property which makes them ideal substances for the production of coins and jewelry.

NONMETALS

Nonmetals are found on the upper-right side of the periodic table. The metals claim that the nonmetals are jealous of them for their shiny hair and sparkly personalities. The nonmetals scoff back, yet quietly steal electrons from them. Nonmetals are generally brittle in the solid state and show little or no metallic luster. They have high ionization energies, electron affinities, and electronegativities, small atomic radii, and are usually poor conductors of heat and electricity. Nonmetals are less unified in their chemical and physical properties than are the metals. They are separated from the metals by a diagonal band of elements called the metalloids.

METALLOIDS

The metalloids are also called the semimetals because they possess characteristics that are between those of metals and nonmetals. The electronegativities and

---

Key Concept

Left → Right
- Atomic radius ↓
- Ionization energy ↑
- Electron affinity ↑
- Electronegativity ↑

Top → Bottom
- Atomic radius ↑
- Ionization energy ↓
- Electron affinity ↓
- Electronegativity ↓

Note: Atomic radius is always opposite the other trends.

MCAT Expertise

The effective nuclear charge, Z_{eff}, can explain all periodic trends as well as chemical properties.

ionization energies of the metalloids lie between those of metals and nonmetals. Their physical properties, such as densities, melting points, and boiling points, vary widely and can be combinations of metallic and nonmetallic characteristics. For example, silicon has a metallic luster but is brittle and a poor conductor. The particular reactivity of the metalloids is dependent upon the elements with which they are reacting. Boron (B), for example, behaves as a nonmetal when reacting with sodium (Na) and as a metal when reacting with fluorine (F). The elements classified as metalloids form a staircase and include boron, silicon, germanium, arsenic, antimony, tellurium, and polonium.

The Chemistry of Groups

ALKALI METALS

The **alkali metals,** Group IA (Group 1), possess most of the classic physical properties of metals, except that their densities are lower than those of other metals (as is true of lithium). The alkali metals have only one loosely bound electron in their outermost shells, and their Z_{eff} values are very low, giving them the largest atomic radii of all the elements in their respective periods. The very low Z_{eff} values also result in low ionization energies, low electron affinities, and low electronegativities, and they easily lose one electron to form univalent cations. They react very readily with nonmetals, especially halogens.

ALKALINE EARTH METALS

The **alkaline earth metals,** Group IIA (Group 2), also possess many properties characteristic of metals. They share most of the characteristics of the alkali metals except that they have slightly higher effective nuclear charges and so have slightly smaller atomic radii. They have two electrons in their valence shell, both of which are easily removed to form divalent cations. Together, the alkali and alkaline earth metals are called the active metals because they are so reactive that they are not naturally found in their elemental (neutral) state.

HALOGENS

The **halogens,** Group VIIA (Group 17), are highly reactive nonmetals with seven valence electrons. They are rather "desperate" to complete their octets by each gaining an additional electron. The halogens are highly variable in their physical properties. For instance, the halogens range from gaseous (F_2 and Cl_2) to liquid (Br_2) to solid (I_2) at room temperature. Their chemical reactivity is more uniform, and due to their very high electronegativities and electron affinities, they are especially reactive toward the alkali and alkaline earth metals. Fluorine has the highest electronegativity of all the elements. The halogens are so reactive that they are not naturally found in their elemental state but rather as ions (called *halides*).

6. The properties of atoms can be predicted, to some extent, by their location within the periodic table. Which property or properties increase in the direction of the arrows shown?

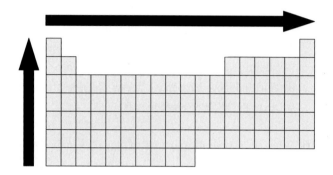

   I. Electronegativity

  II. Atomic radius

 III. First ionization energy

  A. I only

  B. II only

  C. I and III only

  D. II and III only

7. Metals are often used for making wires that conduct electricity. Which of the following properties of metals explains why?

  A. Metals are malleable.

  B. Metals have high electronegativities.

  C. Metals have valence electrons that can move freely.

  D. Metals have high melting points.

8. Which of the following is an important property of the set of elements shaded in the periodic table shown?

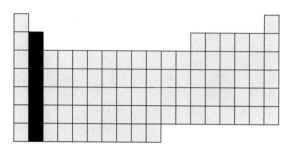

  A. These elements are the best electrical conductors in the periodic table.

  B. These elements form divalent cations.

  C. The second ionization energy for these elements is lower than the first ionization energy.

  D. The atomic radii of these elements decrease as one moves down the column.

9. When dissolved in water, which of the following ions is most likely to form a complex ion with H_2O?

  A. Na^+

  B. Fe^{2+}

  C. Cl^-

  D. S^{2-}

10. How many valence electrons are present in elements in the third period?

  A. 2

  B. 3

  C. The number decreases as the atomic number increases.

  D. The number increases as the atomic number increases.

11. Which of the following elements has the highest electronegativity?

  A. Mg

  B. Cl

  C. Zn

  D. I

12. Of the four atoms depicted here, which has the highest electron affinity?

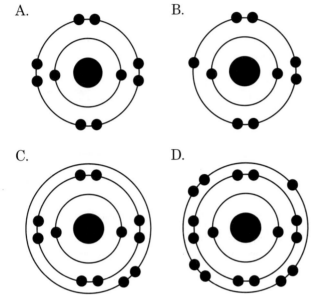

A.

B.

C.

D.

13. Which of the following is true of an atom with a large atomic radius?

   A. The atom is most likely to be on the right side of the periodic table.

   B. The atom is likely to have a high second ionization energy.

   C. The atom is likely to have low electronegativity.

   D. The atom is likely to form ionic bonds.

14. Which of the following atoms/ions has the largest effective nuclear charge?

   A. Cl

   B. Cl⁻

   C. K

   D. K⁺

15. Why do halogens often form ionic bonds with alkaline earth metals?

   A. The alkaline earth metals have much higher electron affinities than the halogens.

   B. By sharing electrons equally, the alkaline earth metals and halogens both form full octets.

   C. Within the same row, the halogens have smaller atomic radii than the alkaline earth metals.

   D. The halogens have much higher electron affinities than the alkaline earth metals.

16. What is the outermost orbital of elements in the third period?

   A. *s*-orbital

   B. *p*-orbital

   C. *d*-orbital

   D. *f*-orbital

Small Group Questions

1. Mercury (Hg) exists as a liquid at room temperature. Why, then, is it classified as a metal? What metallic properties might it possess?

2. The transition metals in group VIIIB could theoretically have eight different oxidation states. In reality, that does not hold true. Why not?

Explanations to Practice Questions

1. B

To answer this question, one must first recall that the periodic table is organized with periods (rows) and groups (columns). This method of organization allows elements to be organized such that some chemical properties can be predicted based on an element's position in the table. Groups (columns) are particularly significant because they represent sets of elements with the same outer electron configuration. In other words, all elements within the same group will have the same configuration of *valence electrons,* which in turn will dictate many of the chemical properties of those similar elements. Although (A) is true, the fact that both ions are positively charged does not explain the similarity in chemical properties as effectively as does answer (B); most other metals, whether or not they are similar to lithium and sodium, produce positively charged ions. (C) is not true, because periods are rows and lithium and sodium are in the same column. Finally, although lithium and sodium do have relatively low atomic weights, so do several other elements that do not share those same properties.

2. A

This question assesses understanding of a key periodic trend: atomic radii. As one moves from left to right across a period (row), atomic radii decrease. This occurs because as more protons are added to the nucleus and more electrons are added within the same shell, there is no increased shielding between the protons and electrons, but there is increased attractive electrostatic force. This effect decreases the atomic radius. In contrast, as one moves from top to bottom down a group (column), extra electron shells accumulate, despite the fact that the valence configurations remain identical. These extra electron shells provide shielding between the positive nucleus and the outermost electrons, decreasing the electrostatic forces and increasing the atomic

radius. Because carbon and silicon are in the same group, and silicon is farther down the periodic table, it will have a larger atomic radius because of its extra electron shell. (C) and (D) are incorrect because all elements in the same group have the same number of valence electrons.

3. C

Atomic radius is determined by multiple factors. Of the choices given, the number of valence electrons does have an impact on the atomic radius. As one moves across a period (row), protons and valence electrons are added, and the electrons are more strongly attracted to the central protons. This attraction tightens the atom, shrinking the atomic radius. The number of electron shells is also significant, as demonstrated by the trend when moving down a group (column). As more electron shells are added that separate the positively charged nucleus from the outermost electrons, the electrostatic forces are weakened and the atomic radius increases. The number of neutrons, III, is irrelevant, because it does not impact these attractive forces. Statements I and II are correct, and III is incorrect.

4. C

Ionization energy is related to the same set of forces that explain atomic radius, as well as the rules governing maintenance of a full valence shell octet. The first set of rules dictates that the stronger the attractive forces between the outer electron (the electron to be ionized) and the positively charged nucleus, the more energy will be required to ionize. As a result, strong attractive forces, which make the atomic radius smaller toward the right of a period or the top of a group, will also increase the first ionization energy. With this information alone, one could guess that ionization energies for beryllium (Be) should be higher than those for Li (lithium), eliminating (A) and (B). How should we choose between the two ionization energies for beryllium? The first ionization energy is usually dramatically lower than the second. This property holds true for the same reasons previously discussed. For example, upon removing one electron from beryllium, the ion is Be^{1+}, which has one more proton in its nucleus than it has electrons surrounding it. Thus, there is a heightened electrostatic force between the positive nucleus and the now less-negative electron cloud, meaning that all remaining electrons will be held more tightly than before. Removing a second electron will be even more difficult than the initial electron removal, making the second ionization energy higher than the first. Furthermore, the first ionization energy for Li is 520.2 kJ/mol, the first ionization energy for Be is 899.5 kJ/mol, and the second ionization energy for Be is 1757.1 kJ/mol.

5. D

Selenium is on the right side of the periodic table (atomic number 34), too far right to be a metal or metalloid. However, it does not lie far enough to the right to fall under column 7A, which would classify it as a halogen.

6. C

The trend in the periodic table demonstrated by the figure is correct for increasing electronegativity and first ionization energy. Electronegativity describes how strong of an attraction an element will have for electrons in a bond. A nucleus with a stronger electrostatic pull due to its positive charge will have a higher electronegativity. An arrow pointing toward the right represents this because effective nuclear charge increases toward the right side of a period. This mirrors the trend for ionization energies, because a stronger nuclear pull will also lead to increased first ionization energy, as the forces make it more difficult to remove an electron. The vertical arrow can be explained by the size of the atoms. As size decreases, the proximity of the outermost electrons to the positive inner nucleus increases, making the positive charge more effective at attracting new electrons in a chemical bond (which leads to higher electronegativity). Similarly, the more effective the positive nuclear charge, the higher the first ionization energy. Because I and III are both correct, we can choose answer choice C.

7. C

All four descriptions of metals are true, but the most significant property that contributes to their ability to conduct electricity is the fact that they have valence electrons that can move freely (C). Large atomic radii, low ionization energies, and low electronegativities all contribute to the ability of metals' outermost electrons to be easily removed, but it's the free movement of electrons that actually conducts the electricity.

8. B

This block represents the alkaline earth metals, which form divalent cations, or ions with a +2 charge. All of the elements in Group IIA have two electrons in their outermost s-orbital. Because loss of these two electrons would then leave a full octet as the outermost shell, becoming a divalent cation is a stable configuration for all of the alkaline earth metals. Although some of these elements might be great conductors, it's an exaggeration to say that they are the best ones on the periodic table, so (A) is incorrect. (C) is also incorrect because although forming a divalent cation is a stable configuration for the alkaline earths, the second ionization energy is still always higher than the first due to the increased positive nuclear charge when compared with the outer negative charge from the electrons. Finally, (D) is incorrect because atomic radii increase when moving down a group of elements because the number of electron shells increases.

9. B

Iron, Fe^{2+}, is a transition metal. Transition metals can often form more than one ion. Iron, for example, can be Fe^{2+} or Fe^{3+}. The transition metals, in these various oxidation states, can often form hydration complexes (complexes with water). Part of the significance of these complexes is that when a transition metal can form a complex, its solubility within the complex solvent will increase. The other ions given might dissolve readily in water, but because none of them are transition metals, they won't form complexes.

10. D

This question is simple if you recall that "periods" name the horizontal rows of the periodic table, while "families" refer to its columns. Within the same period, an additional valence electron is added with each step towards the right side of the table.

11. B

This question requires knowledge of the trends of electronegativity within the periodic table. Electronegativity increases as one moves from left to right across periods, for the same reasons that effective nuclear force increases. Electronegativity *decreases* as one moves down the periodic table, because there are more electron shells separating the nucleus from the outermost electrons. The noble gases, however, also have extremely low electronegativities because they already have full valence shells and do not desire additional electrons. The most electronegative atom in the periodic table is fluorine. The answer choice closest to fluorine is (B), chlorine. Although iodine (D) will be fairly electronegative, its higher atomic radius and position farther down on the periodic table make it less electronegative than Cl. The remaining answer choices, Mg and Li, are elements with very low electronegativities. Because they have only two and one valence electrons, respectively, they are more likely to lose these electrons in a bond than to gain electrons; the loss of electrons would leave them with a full octet. Metals like these are often called electropositive.

12. B

Electron affinity is related to several factors, including atomic size (radius) and filling of the valence shell. As atomic radius increases, the distance between the inner protons in the nucleus and the outermost electrons increases, thereby decreasing the attractive forces between protons and electrons. Additionally, as more electron shells are added from period to period, these shells shield the outermost electrons increasingly from inner protons. As a result, increased atomic radius will lead to lower electron affinity. Because atoms are in a low-energy state when their outermost valence electron shell is filled, atoms needing only one or two electrons to complete this shell will have high electron affinities. In contrast, atoms with already full valence shells (a full octet of electrons) will have very low electron affinity, because adding an extra electron would

require a new shell. With this information, it is clear that (C) and (D) will likely have lower electron affinities than (A) and (B) because there is an extra electron shell "shielding" the nucleus from the outer electrons. Answer (A) is incorrect because its valence electron shell is already full with a complete octet, granting it extremely low electron affinity. Finally, (B) has one electron missing from its outermost shell, as does (D). This valence electron configuration is conducive to wanting to accept electrons readily—or to having a high electron affinity. (B) is the configuration of chlorine, while (D) is bromine. (B) is a better answer than (D), however, because the additional shell of electrons shielding the nucleus in (D) will decrease its electron affinity when compared with (B).

13. C

Electronegativity is the only property listed that has a consistent inverse correlation with atomic radius. Highly electronegative atoms hold bonding electrons tightly, while atoms with low electronegativity hold bonding electrons loosely. In atoms with large atomic radii, the distance between the outermost electrons used for bonding and the central positively charged nucleus is large. This increased distance means that the positively charged nucleus has little ability to attract new, bonding electrons toward it. In comparison, if the atomic radius is small, the force from the positively charged protons will have a stronger effect, because the distance through which they have to act is decreased. (A) is incorrect because atomic radius decreases when moving from left to right across periods in the periodic table. (B) is incorrect because atomic radius alone does not give enough information for one to ascertain the second ionization energy; it is significant to also consider the valence electron configuration. Additionally, all atoms have high second ionization energies. Finally, there is insufficient information supporting (D).

14. D

The effective nuclear charge refers to the strength with which the protons in the nucleus can "pull" additional electrons. This phenomenon helps to explain electron affinity, electronegativity, and ionization energy. In Cl, the nonionized chlorine atom, the nuclear charge is balanced by the surrounding electrons: 17+/17−. The chloride ion, in contrast, has a lower effective nuclear charge, because there are more electrons than protons: 17+/18−. Next, elemental potassium also has a "balanced" effective nuclear charge: 19+/19−. K$^+$, ionic potassium, has a higher effective nuclear charge than any of the other options do, because it has more protons than electrons: 19+/18−. Thus, the potassium ion, (D), is the correct answer.

15.   D
Ionic bonds are bonds formed through unequal sharing of electrons. These bonds typically occur because the electron affinities of the two bonded atoms differ greatly. For example, the halogens have high electron affinities because adding a single electron to their valence shells would create full outer octets. In contrast, the alkaline earth metals have very low electron affinities and are more likely to be electron donors because the loss of one electron would leave them with full outer octets. This marked difference in electron affinity is the best explanation for the formation of ionic bonds between these two different groups. (A) states the opposite and is incorrect, because the halogens have high electron affinity and the alkaline earth metals have low affinity. (B) is incorrect because equal sharing of electrons is a classic description of covalent bonding, not ionic. (C) is a true statement but is not relevant to why ionic bonds form.

16.   C
In the first period, all elements have only an *s*-orbital. In the second period onwards, a 2*p*-orbital is present. In the third period, we find 3*s*-, 3*p*-, and 3*d*-orbitals. Though *3d* appears to be part of the fourth period, it still shares the same principal quantum number as *3s* and *3p* (*n* = 3) and is therefore still applicable.

oxygen, fluorine, sodium, and magnesium. (We include the last two even though they lose—rather than gain—sufficient electrons to end up with a completed octet.)

We classify chemical bonds into two distinct types: ionic and covalent. In **ionic bonding,** one or more electrons from an atom with lower ionization energy, typically a metal, are transferred to an atom with greater electron affinity, typically a nonmetal, and the electrostatic force of attraction between opposite charges holds the resulting ions together. This is the nature of the bond in sodium chloride, where the positively charged sodium **cation** is electrostatically attracted to the negatively charged chloride **anion.** In **covalent bonding,** an electron pair is shared between the two atoms, typically two nonmetals, which have relatively similar values of electronegativity. The actual degree to which the pair of electrons is shared equally or unequally between the two atoms determines the degree of polarity in the covalent bond. If the electron pair is shared equally, the covalent bond is **nonpolar**; if the pair is shared unequally, the bond is **polar.** If both electrons being shared were contributed by only one of the two atoms, the bond is called **coordinate covalent.**

Ionic Bonds

Ionic bonds form between atoms that have significantly different electronegativities. The atom that loses the electron(s) becomes a cation and the atom that gains the electron(s) becomes an anion. The resulting ionic bond is the electrostatic force of attraction between the opposite charges of the ions. There is no sharing of electrons in an ionic bond. In order for this electron transfer to occur, the difference in electronegativity must be greater than 1.7 on the 4.0-Pauling scale. In general, you will recognize ionic bonds forming between the alkali metals and the alkaline earth metals of Groups IA and IIA (Groups 1 and 2), and the halogens of Group VIIA (Group 17). The atoms of the active metals have one or two electrons, which they hold on to only loosely. The atoms of the halogens are strongly "interested in" gaining one more electron to complete their valence shell. These tendencies explain the formation of the ionic bond in, say, sodium chloride, which we've already discussed.

Ionic compounds have characteristic physical properties, which you should recognize for Test Day. Because of the strength of the electrostatic force between the ionic constituents of the compound, ionic compounds have very high melting and boiling points. The melting point of sodium chloride is greater than 800°C. Many ionic compounds dissolve readily in aqueous and other polar solvent solutions, and in the molten or aqueous state are good conductors of electricity. In the solid state, the ionic constituents of the compound form a crystalline lattice consisting of repeating positive and negative ions in which the attractive forces between oppositely charged ions maximize, while the repulsive forces between ions of like charge minimize.

Mnemonic

The *t* in cation looks like a plus sign: ca + ion.

For example, if you were to analyze the atomic structure of the salt you just spread over the meat that you're going to grill up for dinner, you would see that each sodium ion is surrounded by six chloride ions and each chloride is surrounded by six sodium ions. This is a lattice formation known as 6:6 coordinated. (The optimal time to salt meat is about 30 minutes prior to cooking so that the salt has sufficient time to draw fluid to the surface by osmosis, creating a salt solution, which then gets drawn back into the muscle fiber once again. This results in well-seasoned meat through the entire thickness, not just at the surface.)

Covalent Bonds

When two or more atoms with similar electronegativities interact, the energy required to form ions through the complete transfer of one or more electrons is greater than the energy that would be released upon the formation of an ionic bond. That is to say, when two atoms of similar tendency form a compound to attract electrons in a bond, it is energetically unfavorable to form ions. So, rather than struggling to form ions, the atoms simply opt to share the electrons as a compromise, which allows them both to fill their valence shells. The binding force between the atoms is not ionic; rather, it is the attraction that each electron in the shared pair has for the two positive nuclei of the bonded atoms.

Covalent compounds contain discrete molecular units with relatively weak intermolecular interactions. Consequently, these compounds tend to have lower melting and boiling points, and because they do not break down into constituent ions, they are poor conductors of electricity in the liquid state or in aqueous solutions.

PROPERTIES OF COVALENT BONDS

The formation of one covalent bond may not be sufficient to fill the valence shell for a given atom. Thus many atoms can form bonds with more than one other atom and each atom can form multiple bonds between itself and another atom, with few exceptions. Two atoms sharing one, two, or three pairs of electrons are said to be joined by a single, double, or triple covalent bond, respectively. The number of shared electron pairs between two atoms is called the bond order; hence a single bond has a bond order of one, a double bond has a bond order of two, and a triple bond has a bond order of three. Three features characterize a covalent bond: bond length, bond energy, and polarity.

Bond Length

If the arrangement of atoms in covalent bonds can be likened to two wooden spools connected by a dowel in a very sophisticated children's construction set, then the length of the dowel is analogous to the length of the bond between the atoms sharing the electron pair(s). Bond length is the average distance between

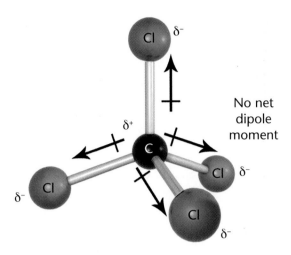

Figure 3.5

However, when the molecular geometry is such that the bond dipoles do not cancel each other, the molecule will have a net dipole moment and therefore will be polar. For instance, the O–H bonds in H_2O are polar, with each hydrogen molecule assuming a partial positive charge and the oxygen assuming a partial negative charge. Because water's molecular geometry is angular (bent), the vector summation of the bond dipoles results in a molecular dipole moment from the partially positive hydrogen end to the partially negative oxygen end, as illustrated in Figure 3.6.

> **Key Concept**
>
> A molecule with polar bonds need not be polar: The bond dipole moments may cancel each other out, resulting in a nonpolar molecule. Although a molecule with polar bonds need not be polar overall, a polar molecule must have polar bonds.

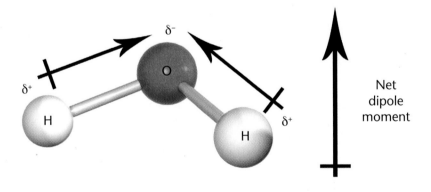

Figure 3.6

ATOMIC AND MOLECULAR ORBITALS

In order to finish our discussion of covalent bonds, we need to address the issue of atomic and molecular orbitals. If you remember back to the first chapter, we described the modern understanding of the atom as a dense, positively charged nucleus surrounded by clouds of electrons organized into orbitals (regions in space surrounding the nucleus within which there are certain probabilities of finding an electron). The four quantum numbers completely describe the energy and position

Bridge

Quantum Numbers (Chapter 1) revisited:

- For any value of *n*, there are *n* values of *l* (0 → *n* − 1).

- *l* = 0 → *s*
  l = 1 → *p*
  l = 2 → *d*

- For any value of *l*, there are 2*l* + 1 values of m_l (number of orbitals); values themselves will range from −*l* to *l*.

of any electron of an atom. While the principal quantum number indicates the average energy level of the orbitals, the azimuthal quantum number, *l*, describes the subshells within each principal energy level, *n*. When *l* = 0, this indicates the *s*-subshell, which has one orbital that is spherical in shape. The 1*s*-orbital (*n* = 1, *l* = 1) is plotted in Figure 3.7.

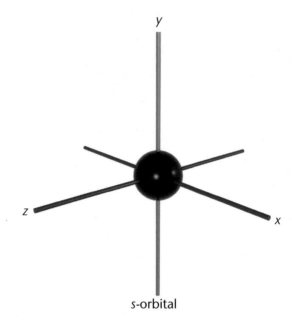

s-orbital

Figure 3.7

When *l* = 1, this indicates the *p*-subshell, which has three orbitals shaped like barbells along the *x, y,* and *z* axes at right angles to each other. The *p*-orbitals are plotted in Figure 3.8.

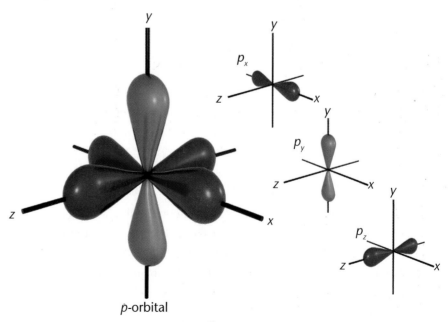

p-orbital

Figure 3.8

Although well beyond the scope of the MCAT, mathematical analyses of the wave function of the orbitals are used to determine and assign plus and minus signs to each lobe of the *p*-orbitals. The shapes of the five *d*-orbitals and the seven *f*-orbitals are more complex and need not be memorized for the MCAT. When two atoms bond to form a compound, the atomic orbitals interact to form a molecular orbital that describes the probability of finding the bonding electrons. Molecular orbitals are obtained by combining the wave functions of the atomic orbitals. Qualitatively, the overlap of two atomic orbitals describes this. If the signs of the two atomic orbitals are the same, a bonding orbital forms. If the signs are different, an antibonding orbital forms.

Two different patterns of overlap are observed in the formation of molecular bonds. When orbitals overlap head-to-head, the resulting bond is called a sigma (σ) bond. Sigma bonds allow for relatively free rotation because the electron density of the bonding orbital is a single linear accumulation between the atomic nuclei. When the orbitals overlap in such a way that there are two parallel electron cloud densities, a pi (π) bond is formed. Pi bonds do not allow for free rotation because the electron densities of the orbital are parallel. To picture this difference, imagine pushing your fists together and rotating them as they touch—this is a sigma bond. Now imagine putting your arms out in front of you, holding them parallel to each other with your elbows bent at about right angles while another person slips two rubber bands around your forearms, one near the elbows and the second closer to the wrists. With the rubber bands on, try bringing one forearm up toward you while you extend your other forearm out away from you. The parallel tension provided by the rubber bands makes it quite difficult to rotate your forearms in opposite directions. This is a pi bond.

The Intermolecular Forces

Like guests at a cocktail party who mingle together but ultimately have little to say to each other, atoms and compounds interact with each other through weak electrostatic interactions. The strength of these intermolecular interactions can impact certain physical properties of the compounds such as melting and boiling point. The weakest of the intermolecular interactions are the dispersion forces, also known as London forces. Next, are the dipole-dipole interactions, which are of intermediate strength. Finally, we have the strongest type of interaction, the hydrogen bond, which is a misnomer because there is no sharing or transfer of electrons, and consequently, it is not a true bond. We must keep in mind, however, that even hydrogen bonds, the strongest of these interactions, have only about 10 percent the strength of a covalent bond, so these electrostatic interactions can be overcome with additions of small or moderate amounts of energy.

> **Bridge**
>
> The pi bonds of alkenes, alkynes, aromatic compounds, and carboxylic acid derivates are what lend the ever-important functionalities in organic chemistry.

> **Bridge**
>
> These intermolecular forces are the binding forces that keep a substance together in its solid or liquid state (see Chapter 8). These same forces determine whether two substances are miscible or immiscible in the solution phase (see Chapter 9).

LONDON FORCES

The bonding electrons in nonpolar covalent bonds may appear, on paper, to be shared equally between two atoms, but at any point in time they will be located randomly throughout the orbital. For these instantaneous moments, then, the electron density may be unequally distributed between the two atoms. This results in rapid polarization and counterpolarization of the electron cloud and the formation of short-lived dipole moments. These dipoles interact with the electron clouds of neighboring compounds, inducing the formation of more dipoles. The momentarily negative end of one molecule will cause the closest region in any neighboring molecule to become temporarily positive itself, thus causing the other end of this neighboring molecule to become temporarily negative, which in turn induces other molecules to become temporarily polarized, and the entire process begins all over again. The attractive interactions of these short-lived and rapidly shifting dipoles are called **dispersion forces** or **London forces.**

Dispersion forces are the weakest of all the intermolecular interactions because they are the result of induced dipoles that change and shift moment by moment. They do not extend over long distances, and are therefore significant only when molecules are close together. The strength of the London force also depends on the degree to which and the ease by which the molecules can be polarized (that is to say, how easily the electrons can be shifted around). Large molecules in which the electrons are far from the nucleus are relatively easy to polarize and therefore possess greater dispersion forces. Think about two plates—a big dinner plate and a small teacup saucer—with nearly equal numbers of marbles on each. The marbles will roll around more, and may be distributed more unequally, on the bigger plate than on the smaller saucer. Nevertheless, don't underestimate the importance of the dispersion forces. If it weren't for them, the noble gases would not liquefy at any temperature because no other intermolecular forces exist between the noble gas atoms. The low temperatures at which the noble gases liquefy is to some extent indicative of the magnitude of the dispersion forces between the atoms.

DIPOLE–DIPOLE INTERACTIONS

Polar molecules tend to orient themselves in such a way that the opposite ends of the respective molecular dipoles are closest to each other: the positive region of one molecule is close to the negative region of another molecule. This arrangement is energetically favorable because an attractive electrostatic force is formed between the two molecules.

Dipole–dipole interactions are present in the solid and liquid phases but become negligible in the gas phase because of the significantly increased distance of separation between gas particles. Polar species tend to have higher melting and boiling

Real World

While London forces (a type of van der Waals force) are the weakest of the intermolecular attractions, when there are millions of these interactions, as there are on the bottom of a gecko's foot, there is an amazing power of adhesion that is demonstrated by the animal's ability to climb smooth vertical, even inverted, surfaces.

points than those of nonpolar species of comparable molecular weight. You should realize that London forces and dipole–dipole interactions are different not in kind, but in degrees. Both are electrostatic forces between opposite partial charges; the difference is only in the strength and in the permanence of the molecular dipole.

HYDROGEN BONDS

Hydrogen bonds are a favorite of the MCAT! So understand them well, and you will be able to answer every question pertaining to their nature, behavior, and effects. A hydrogen bond is actually only a specific, unusually strong form of dipole-dipole interaction, which may be intra- or intermolecular. Please understand that hydrogen bonds are not actually bonds—there is no sharing or transfer of electrons between two atoms. When hydrogen is bound to a highly electronegative atom such as fluorine, oxygen, or nitrogen, the hydrogen atom carries little of the electron density of the covalent bond. The hydrogen atom acts essentially as a naked proton (it is a *little* scandalous!). The positively charged hydrogen atom interacts with the partial negative charge of oxygen, nitrogen, or fluorine on nearby molecules. Substances that display hydrogen bonding tend to have unusually high boiling points compared with compounds of similar molecular formula that do not hydrogen bond. The difference derives from the energy required to break the hydrogen bonds. A very good example of this difference, which you absolutely need to understand for the MCAT, is the difference between a carboxylic acid, which can form hydrogen bonds between molecules of itself, and the acyl halide, a derivative of the carboxylic acid, which has substituted a halogen for the hydroxyl group, and which cannot form hydrogen bonds between molecules of itself. The boiling point of propanoic acid (*mw* = 74 g/mol) is 141°C, but the boiling point of propanoyl chloride (*mw* = 92.5 g/mol) is 80°C. Hydrogen bonding is particularly important in the behavior of water, alcohols, amines, and carboxylic acids. It is no overstatement to say that if it weren't for water's ability to form hydrogen bonds and exist in the liquid state at room temperature, we would not exist (at least not in the form we recognize as "human").

Conclusion

This chapter built upon our knowledge of the atom and the trends demonstrated by the elements in the periodic table to understand the different ways by which atoms partner together to form compounds, either exchanging electrons to form ions that are then held together by the electrostatic force of attraction that exists between opposite charges, or sharing electrons to form covalent bonds. We discussed the nature and characteristics of covalent bonds, noting their relative lengths and energies as well as polarities. The review of Lewis structures and VSEPR theory will prepare you for predicting likely bond arrangements, resonance structures, and molecular geometry. Finally, we compared the relative strengths of the most important intermolecular electrostatic interactions, noting that even the strongest of these, the hydrogen bond, is still much weaker than an actual covalent bond. The next time you're searing meat in a skillet or browning toast in a toaster, take a moment to consider what's actually going on at the atomic and molecular level. It's not just cooking; it's science!

CONCEPTS TO REMEMBER

☐ Atoms come together to form compounds through bonds. Many atoms interact with other atoms in order to achieve the octet electron configuration in their valence shell. There are two types of bonds: ionic and covalent.

☐ Ionic bonds form when a very electronegative atom gains one or more electrons from a much less electronegative atom, and the strong electrostatic force of attraction between opposite charges holds the resulting anion and cation together. Covalent bonds form when two atoms share one or more pairs of electrons. The force of the bond is due to the electrostatic attraction between the electrons in the bond and each of the positively charged nuclei of the bonding atoms.

☐ Covalent bonds are characterized by their length, energy, and polarity. A single covalent bond exists when two atoms share one pair of electrons; a double bond exists when two atoms share two pairs of electrons; and a triple bond exists when two atoms share three pairs of electrons. Triple bonds are the shortest and have the highest bond energy. Single bonds are the longest and have the lowest bond energy.

☐ Although all covalent bonds involve a sharing of one or more electron pairs, the electron density of the bonding electrons may not be distributed equally between the bonding atoms. This gives rise to a polar bond, with the more electronegative atom receiving the larger share of the bonding electron density.

☐ Lewis structures are bookkeeping devices used to keep track of the valence electrons of atoms and their various possible different arrangements in a compound. Evaluation of formal charge on each atom in the arrangement can help determine which arrangement is most likely to be representative of the actual bond connectivity. Lewis structures that demonstrate the same atomic arrangement but differ in the distribution of electron pairs are called resonance structures. The actual molecular positioning of electrons is a "weighted" hybrid of all the possible resonance structures called a resonance hybrid.

☐ VSEPR theory helps us predict the actual three-dimensional arrangement of bonded and nonbonded electron pairs around the central atom in a compound. The theory states that nonbonded electrons (lone pairs) exert strong electrostatic repulsive forces against the bonded pairs of electrons and, as a result, the electron pairs arrange themselves as far apart as possible in order to minimize the repulsive forces.

☐ A molecular dipole is the resultant of all the bond dipole vectors in the molecule. A compound consisting of only nonpolar bonds will by definition be nonpolar. A compound consisting of one polar bond will by definition be polar (although perhaps insignificantly). A compound consisting of two or more polar bonds may be polar or nonpolar depending on the molecular geometry and the vector addition of the bond dipoles.

☐ Atomic orbitals overlap their + and − lobes to result in bonding or antibonding molecular orbitals. When the signs of the overlapping atomic orbitals are the same, the result is a bonding molecular orbital. When the signs are opposite, the result is an antibonding orbital.

☐ Sigma bonds involve head-to-head (or end-to-end) overlap of electron cloud density and thus allow for relatively low-energy rotation. Pi bonds involve parallel overlap of electron cloud density and thus do not allow for low-energy rotation.

☐ The intermolecular interactions are electrostatic interactions that weakly hold molecules together. They generally are significant only over short distances and in the solid or liquid state. The weakest intermolecular interaction is the dispersion force (London force), which results from the moment-by-moment changing unequal distribution of the electron cloud density across molecules. A more moderate-strength intermolecular interaction is the dipole–dipole interaction, which exists between the opposite ends of permanent molecular dipoles. The strongest of these intermolecular interactions is the hydrogen bond, which is a special case of the dipole–dipole interaction between the hydrogen atom attached to either oxygen, nitrogen, or fluorine, and another oxygen, nitrogen, or fluorine on another—and sometimes, if the molecule is large enough, even the same molecule. One of the most important occurrences of hydrogen bonding is that between water molecules.

EQUATIONS TO REMEMBER

☐ $\mu = qr$

☐ Formal Charge $= V - N_{nonbonding} - \frac{1}{2}N_{bonding}$

these molecules in close proximity to one another. So which boils at a higher temperature? Alcohols are known for their ability to hydrogen bond, which significantly raises boiling point. Hydrogen bonding occurs when an electronegative atom (fluorine, oxygen, or nitrogen) binds to hydrogen, stripping it of electron density and leaving it with a partial positive charge. That partial positive charge can then associate with nearby partial negative charges. These forces are even stronger than dipole–dipole interactions, so isopropyl alcohol will boil at a higher temperature than acetone. Finally, the strongest interactions are ionic, and exist in compounds such as potassium chloride (II).

5. C

The central atom in CO_3, carbon, has no lone pairs. It has three resonance structures, each of which involves a double bond between carbon and one of the three oxygens. Having made four bonds, carbon has no further orbitals for bonding or to carry lone pairs. This makes CO_3's geometry trigonal planar. Alternatively, ClF_3 also has three bonds, one to each of three fluoride atoms. However, chloride still maintains two extra lone pairs (without which the formal charge on the central chloride atom is +4; with the two lone pairs it is zero, a more stable configuration). These lone pairs each inhabit one orbital, meaning that the central chloride must organize five items about itself: three bonds to fluorides and two lone pairs. The best configuration for maximizing the distance between all of these groups is trigonal bipyramidal. (A) is true, but does not account for the difference in geometry. Similarly, although (B) is true, the charge does not explain a difference in geometry. (D) is incorrect; CO_3 has no lone pairs on its central atom, while ClF_3 has two lone pairs.

6. A

The best way to approach this problem is to draw the structure of each of these molecules, and then consider the electronegativity of each bond as it might contribute to an overall dipole moment. HCN is the correct answer because of large differences in electronegativity, aligned in a linear fashion. There is a strong dipole moment in the direction of nitrogen, without any other moments canceling it out. H_2O has two dipole moments, one from each hydrogen pointing in the direction of oxygen. The molecule is bent, and the dipole moments partially cancel out. There *is* a molecular dipole, but it is not as strong as HCN's. Sulfur dioxide has a similar bent configuration, so its dipole will be smaller than that of HCN. Another consideration for sulfur dioxide is that oxygen and sulfur do not have a large difference in electronegativity, so even the individual bond dipoles are smaller than those we have seen so far. CCl_4 has a tetrahedral geometry. Although each of the individual C–Cl bonds is highly polar, the orientation of these bonds causes the dipoles to fully cancel each other out, yielding no overall dipole moment.

7. D

Bond lengths decrease as the bond order increases, and also decrease in a trend moving up the periodic table's columns or to the right across to the periodic table's rows. In this case, because both C_2H_2 and NCH have triple bonds, we cannot compare the bond lengths based upon bond order. We must then rely on other periodic trends. The bond length decreases when moving to the right along the periodic table's rows because more electronegative atoms have shorter atomic radii. The nitrogen in NCH is likely to hold its electrons closer, or in a shorter radius, than the carbon in C_2H_2. (B) is incorrect because there are no significant resonance structures contributing to the character of either triple bond. (C) expresses a true statement, but one that is irrelevant to the length of the carbon–carbon triple bond.

8. C

(C) correctly describes the underlying forces of hydrogen bonding. Electronegative atoms bound to hydrogen disproportionately pull covalently bonded electrons toward themselves, which leaves hydrogen with a partial positive character. That partial positive charge is attracted to nearby negative or partial-negative charges, such as those on other electronegative atoms. (A) is not true; hydrogen has little electronegativity and does not hold its valence electrons closely. (B) is a true statement but not descriptive enough to explain hydrogen bonding. (D) is not correct; although these bonds are highly polarized, they are not ionic.

9. D

First recall that ammonium is NH_4^+, while ammonia (commonly confused) is NH_3. It helps to associate the suffix "-ium" with a charged form of the molecule. Once you remember that ammonium is NH_4^+, eliminate any answer choice that only accounts for three bonds (answer choice A). Next, it helps to recall that ammonium is formed by the association of NH_3 (uncharged, with a lone pair on the nitrogen) with a positively charge hydrogen cation (no lone pairs). In other worse, NH_3 is a Lewis base, while H^+ is a Lewis acid. This type of bonding, between Lewis acid and base, is a coordinate covalent bond. Thus you know that there is one coordinate covalent bond in this molecule, making (D) the correct answer.

10. C

This question addresses the issue of when the octet rule can be violated. All atoms that are in the third or higher period have d-orbitals, each of which can hold 10 electrons. The typical eight "octet" electrons reside in s- and p-orbitals. (A) and (B) do not explain why more than eight electrons can be held. Electronegativity is irrelevant to whether or not an atom can exceed the octet rule, making (D) incorrect.

11. C

All of the listed types of forces dictate interactions among different types of molecules. However, noble gases are entirely uncharged and do not have polar covalent bonds, ionic bonds, or dipole moments. Recognize that the only types of forces listed that could relate to noble gases could be van der Waals forces (A); or dispersion forces (C). Of these two, van der Waals forces is an umbrella term that includes both dispersion and dipole–dipole interactions (which you've already eliminated). Because not all van der Waals forces apply, rule that out as the correct answer and stick with dispersion forces. Dispersion forces refer specifically to a type of interaction that occurs among all bonded atoms, due to the unequal sharing of electrons at any given moment in the electron's orbit. This unequal sharing allows for instantaneous partial positive and partial negative charges within the molecule. Though these interactions are small, they are necessary for liquefaction.

12. B

The key to this question is understanding the pattern of filling for s- and d-orbitals among the transition metals. There are 24 electrons in chromium, six more than are present in argon. Where will these six electrons lie? It is advantageous for d-orbitals to be half-filled. Therefore, one electron will fill each of the five $3d$-orbitals. It will take less energy to put the sixth electron into an s-orbital than it would to add it to one of the d-orbitals that already has an electron (and force it to no longer be half-filled).

13. A

In this Lewis diagram, the PO_4^{3-} molecule has an overall formal charge of -3. The four oxygens each would be assigned a formal change of -1, based on the following formula: formal charge = V (valence electrons in the free atom) $-\frac{1}{2} N_{bonding}$ (electrons shared in bonds) $-N_{nonbonding}$ (lone pairs/free electrons). For each oxygen, we calculate: FC = $6 - \frac{1}{2}(2) - 6 = -1$. For the central phosphorus, assume then that with a total formal charge of -3 and four oxygens with a change of -1 each, the phosphorus must have a formal charge of $+1$. Alternatively, calculate its formal charge as FC = $5 - \frac{1}{2}(8) - 0 = +1$. Considering this molecule's other resonance structures, you'd come to the same conclusion— that phosphorus is the most positive atom.

14. C

The reaction in this question shows a water molecule, which has two lone pairs of electrons on the central oxygen, combining with a free hydrogen ion. The resulting molecule, H_3O^+, has formed a new bond between H^+ and H_2O. This bond is created through the sharing one of oxygen's lone pairs with the free H^+ ion. This is essentially a donation of a shared pair of electrons from a Lewis base (H_2O) to a Lewis acid (H^+, electron acceptor). The charge in the resulting molecule is $+1$, and is mostly present on the central oxygen, which now only has one lone pair. This type of bond, formed from a Lewis acid and Lewis base, is called a coordinate covalent bond.

15. B

NH_3 has three hydrogen atoms bonded to the central nitrogen, and one lone pair on the central nitrogen. These four groups—three atoms, one lone pair—lead NH_3 to be sp^3 hybridized. By hybridizing all three p-orbitals and the one s-orbital, four groups are arranged about the central atom, maximizing the distance between the groups to minimize the energy of the configuration. NH_3's hybridization leads to its tetrahedral electronic geometry, yet trigonal pyramidal molecular geometry. In contrast, BF_3 has three atoms, but no lone pairs, resulting in sp^2 hybridization. Its shape is called trigonal planar. (A) is incorrect; although BF_3 does has three bonded atoms and no lone pairs, its geometry is not trigonal pyramidal. (C) is tempting because NH_3 has a lone pair, but this answer choice is not complete enough to explain the differences in molecular geometry. Finally, although (D) is also true, the polarity of the molecules does not explain their geometry; rather, the molecules' different geometries contribute to the overall polarity of the molecules.

16. B

Most atoms require eight valence electrons to follow the octet rule. However, some atoms, like beryllium, can have fewer than eight valence electrons (suboctet). As a result, when bonding with chloride, beryllium is likely to form only two bonds, using its own two outer valence electrons and one from each chloride to form $BeCl_2$, as drawn in (B). (A) is incorrect because Be cannot both bond to chloride *and* have lone pairs. (C) assumes that all three atoms need their octets filled, and (D) places 10 electrons on each chlorine.

17. B

This answer requires an understanding of the trends that cause higher or lower bond energies. Bonds of high energy are those that are difficult to break. These bonds tend to have more shared pairs of electrons, and thus cause a stronger attraction between the two atoms in the bonds. This stronger attraction also means that the bond length of a high-energy, high-order bond (i.e., a triple bond) is shorter than that of its lower-energy counterparts (i.e., single or double bonds). Thus, (A) is incorrect; bond energy increases with *decreasing* bond length. Single bonds

are longer than double bonds, thus (C) is incorrect; single bonds are *easier* to break than double bonds. Finally, as previously discussed, bond energy *is* inversely related to bond length, making (D) incorrect.

18. A

Polarity is precisely described by the first answer choice. Dipole moments describe the relationship of shared electrons between two bonded atoms. If there is a dipole moment between two atoms, then the electrons in their shared bond are preferentially centered on one atom, typically the more electronegative of the two. The polarity of a molecule is then defined as the vector sum of these dipole moments in the molecule's three-dimensional configuration. For example, although individual carbon-chloride bonds have dipole moments with a partial negative charge on chloride, the molecule CCl_4 has a tetrahedral configuration and thus the three polarized bonds cancel each other out for no net dipole moment, creating a nonpolar molecule. Based on this description, it is clear that (B) is incorrect, because molecular geometry is an essential component of determining molecular polarity. For the same reasons described previously, it is possible for a nonpolar molecule to contain one or more polar bonds, making (C) incorrect. Finally, it is possible for a molecule to contain at least one nonpolar bond and yet be a polar molecule. For example, CH_3CH_2Cl has a nonpolar bond (C–C), yet a molecular dipole exists. In its tetrahedral arrangement, the one polar bond between C–Cl will have a dipole moment, creating a net polarity of the molecule in the direction of the chloride atom.

Compounds and Stoichiometry

Oh—what is that smell? You and your mother are taking an afternoon walk through the public rose garden, a pleasant activity for a pleasant summer day, and everything was so pleasant until you smelled . . . it, whatever *it* is. Your mother doesn't have to wonder long until her own olfactory system is screeching the alarm, too. *Oh, it's just horrible. It smells like rancid almonds.* Although your better instincts tell you to walk quickly away, you pause and, holding your breath, crouch down to get a better look. You are a premed, after all, and you did just synthesize cinnamaldehyde in your orgo lab, so your curiosity is understandable.

Scanning the leaves of some plants at the base of the rosebush, you notice a few green bugs whose backs give the impression of a shield. A small stick lies temptingly close to your foot. You can't resist and so you grab the stick and position it for optimal poking, but just as the pointy end gets within a few inches of the insect, which now senses that its own pleasant afternoon is about to be ruined, it raises its hind quarters in the direction of the stick, that is to say, in your direction, exposing its sophisticated defense weaponry. *Stink bugs!* you exclaim, as you drop the stick and take what you believe are a sufficient number of steps to remove yourself from the bug's bombing range.

Our world is filled with aromas and odors, some pleasant and some not so much. What is it that we are smelling when we "smell something"? Well, every odor that we perceive is the result of an interaction between the chemical receptors of our olfactory systems and some chemical compound. A stink bug "stinks" because it produces a highly concentrated solution of volatile compounds that we (and anything else that would dare to disturb it) perceive as malodorous, noxious, and irritating. It's a pretty ingenious defense system: make yourself so disgusting, so distasteful, that everyone will leave you alone, or at least think twice before bothering or eating you. Interestingly enough, the primary compounds in the stink bug's stink bomb are hydrogen cyanide (a highly toxic compound that inhibits cytochrome c oxidase, thereby blocking aerobic respiration) and benzaldehyde.

Wait, benzaldehyde? Yes, benzaldehyde—that relatively simple compound consisting of a benzene ring substituted with an aldehyde functional group. You need to recognize it for the Biological Sciences section of the MCAT. Remember that we classify benzene ring compounds as part of the larger class of molecules called aromatic compounds. Therefore, you can smell benzaldehyde because it is aromatic, and like some other aromatic compounds, it vaporizes at room temperature and reaches your olfactory system as gas particles. Now, you might be surprised to learn that benzaldehyde is the key ingredient in artificial almond extract. At low concentrations, it gives a pleasant aroma of toasted almonds. However, at high concentrations, its odor is that of rotten, stinking almonds and is a noxious irritant to skin, eyes, and the respiratory tract. We do not recommend stink bug juice as a suitable cooking substitute for almond extract.

Benzaldehyde is a compound composed of seven carbon atoms, six hydrogen atoms, and one oxygen atom. One mole of benzaldehyde has a mass of 106.12 grams. It can react with other atoms or compounds to form new compounds (pure substances composed of two or more elements in a fixed proportion). They can be broken down by chemical means to produce their constituent elements or other compounds. They are characterized according to the same systems of traits: physical properties and chemical reactivities.

This chapter focuses on compounds and their reactions. It reviews the various ways in which compounds are represented: empirical and molecular formulas and percent composition will be defined and explained. There is a brief overview of the major classes of chemical reactions that we will examine more closely in subsequent chapters, and finally, there is a recap of the steps involved in balancing chemical equations with a particular focus on identifying limiting reagents and calculating reaction yields.

Molecules and Moles

A molecule is a combination of two or more atoms held together by covalent bonds. It is the smallest unit of a compound that displays the identifying properties of that compound. Molecules can be composed of two atoms of the same element, e.g., N_2 and O_2, or may be composed of two or more atoms of different elements, as in CO_2, $SOCl_2$, and C_6H_5CHO (benzaldehyde). Because reactions usually involve a very large number of molecules, far too many to count individually, we usually measure amounts of compounds in terms of moles or grams, using molecular weight to interconvert between these units.

Ionic compounds do not form true molecules because of the way in which the oppositely charged ions arrange themselves in the solid state. As solids, they can be considered as nearly infinite, three-dimensional arrays of the charged particles that comprise the compound. Remember, we mentioned that NaCl, in the solid state, is a 6:6 coordinated lattice in which each of the Na^+ ions is surrounded by six Cl^- ions and each of the Cl^- ions is surrounded by six Na^+ ions. As you might imagine, this makes it rather difficult to clearly define a sodium chloride molecular unit. Because no molecule actually exists, molecular weight becomes meaningless, and the term *formula weight* is used instead. (However, this is a technical distinction over which you ought not to sacrifice too much sleep.)

MOLECULAR WEIGHT

We've mentioned already that the term *atomic weight* is a misnomer, because it is a measurement of mass, not weight (another distinction not worth any sacrifice of sleep), and the same applies, here, to our discussion of **molecular weight**: it's really

Bridge

Ionic compounds form from combinations of elements with large electronegativity differences (that sit far apart on the periodic table), such as sodium and chlorine. Molecular compounds form from the combination of elements of similar electronegativity (that sit close to each other on the periodic table), such as carbon with oxygen.

a measurement of mass. Molecular weight, then, is simply the sum of the atomic weights of all the atoms in a molecule, and its units are atomic mass units (amu). Similarly, the **formula weight** of an ionic compound is found by adding up the atomic weights of the constituent ions according to its empirical formula (see the following example), and its units are grams.

Example: What is the molecular weight of $SOCl_2$?

Solution: To find the molecular weight of $SOCl_2$, add together the atomic weights of each of the atoms.

$$
\begin{array}{lll}
1S = 1 \times 32 \text{ amu} & = & 32 \text{ amu} \\
1O = 1 \times 16 \text{ amu} & = & 16 \text{ amu} \\
2Cl = 2 \times 35.5 \text{ amu} & = & \underline{71 \text{ amu}} \\
\text{molecular weight} & = & 119 \text{ amu}
\end{array}
$$

MOLE

We defined the term *mole* in Chapter 1, Atomic Structure, but let's briefly review it again. A **mole** is a quantity of any thing (molecules, atoms, dollar bills, chairs, etc.) equal to the number of particles that are found in 12 grams of carbon-12. That seems like an awfully strange point of comparison, so all you really need to remember is that "mole" is a quick way of indicating that we have an amount of particles equal to **Avogadro's number**, 6.022×10^{23}. One mole of a compound has a mass in grams equal to the molecular weight of the compound expressed in amu, and contains 6.022×10^{23} molecules of that compound. For example, 62 grams of H_2CO_3 (carbonic acid) represents one mole of the acid compound and contains 6.022×10^{23} molecules of H_2CO_3. The mass of one mole of a compound is called its molar weight or molar mass, and is usually expressed as g/mol. Therefore, the molar mass of H_2CO_3 is 62 g/mol. You may be accustomed to using the term *molecular weight* to imply molar mass. Technically this is not correct, but nobody is going to rap your knuckles with a ruler for this minor infraction.

Real World

Here we mention Avogadro's number again and can see that the mole is just a unit of convenience, like the dozen is a convenient unit for eggs.

The formula for determining the number of moles of a substance present is:

$$\text{mol} = \text{Weight of Sample (g)/Molar Weight (g/mol)}$$

Example: How many moles are in 9.52 g of $MgCl_2$?

Solution: First, find the molar mass of $MgCl_2$.

$$1(24.31 \text{ g/mol}) + 2(35.45 \text{ g/mol}) = 95.21 \text{ g/mol}$$

Now, solve for the number of moles.

$$\frac{9.52}{95.21 \text{ g/mol}} = 0.10 \text{ mol of } MgCl_2$$

EQUIVALENT WEIGHT

Equivalent weight and the related concept of equivalents are a source of confusion for many students. Part of the problem may be the context in which equivalents and equivalent weights are discussed: acid-base reactions, redox reactions, and precipitation reactions, all three of which themselves can be sources of much student confusion and anxiety. So, let's start with some very basic discussion and then, in later chapters, we will see how these concepts and calculations apply to these three types of reactions.

Bridge

The idea of *equivalents* is similar to the concept of normality, which we will see when we study Acids and Bases in Chapter 10.

Generally, some compounds or elements have different capacities to act in certain ways. Not in characteristics or behaviors like electronegativity or ionization energy, but rather the ability of certain elements or compounds to act more potently than others in performing certain reactions. For example, one mole of HCl has the ability to donate one mole of hydrogen ions (H^+) in solution, but one mole of H_2SO_4 has the ability to donate two moles of hydrogen ions, and one mole of H_3PO_4 has the ability to donate three moles of hydrogen ions. Another example to consider is the difference between Na and Mg: one mole of sodium has the ability to donate one mole of electrons, while one mole of magnesium has the ability to donate two moles of electrons. To find one mole of hydrogen ions for a particular acid-base reaction we could "source" those protons from one mole of HCl, or we could instead use a half-mole of H_2SO_4. If we're using H_3PO_4, we'd only need one-third of a mole. This is what we mean by "different capacities to act in certain ways": if we need only one mole of hydrogen ions, it would be a waste to use an entire mole of H_3PO_4, which could donate three times what we need. We are defining the concept of **equivalents**: how many moles of the "thing we are interested in" (i.e., protons, hydroxide ions, electrons, or ions) will the number of moles of the compound present produce? One mole of hydrogen ions (one equivalent) will be donated by one mole of HCl, but two moles of hydrogen ions (two equivalents) will be donated by one mole of H_2SO_4, and three moles of hydrogen ions (three equivalents) will be donated by one mole of H_3PO_4. Simply put, an equivalent is a mole of charge.

Having discussed the concept of equivalents, we can now introduce a calculation that will be helpful on the MCAT, especially for problems of acid-base chemistry. So far, this discussion has been focused on the mole-to-mole relationship between, say, an acid compound and the hydrogen ions it donates. However, sometimes we need to work in units of mass rather than moles. Just as one mole of HCl will donate one mole (one equivalent) of hydrogen ions, a certain mass amount of HCl will donate one equivalent of hydrogen ions. This amount of compound, measured in grams, that produces one equivalent of the monovalent particle of interest (protons, hydroxide ions, electrons, or ions) is called the **gram equivalent weight,** and the equation is:

$$\text{Gram Equivalent Weight} = \text{Molar Mass}/n$$

where n is the number of protons, hydroxide ions, electrons, or monovalent ions "produced" or "consumed" per molecule of the compound in the reaction. For example, you would need 46 grams of H_2SO_4 (molar mass = 98 g/mol) to produce one equivalent of hydrogen ions, because each molecule of H_2SO_4 can donate two hydrogen ions ($n = 2$). Simply put, an equivalent weight of a compound is the mass that provides one mole of charge.

If the amount of a compound in a reaction is known and you need to determine how many equivalents are present, use the following equation:

Equivalents = Mass of Compound (g)/Gram Equivalent Weight (g)

Finally, we can now introduce the measurement of normality without too much fear of causing the almost-always-fatal head explosion. Normality, as the term suggests, is a measure of concentration. The units for normality are equivalents/liter. A 1 N solution of acid contains a concentration of hydrogen ions equal to 1 mole/liter; a 2 N solution of acid contains a concentration of hydrogen ions equal to 2 moles/liter. The actual concentration of the acidic compound may be the same or different from the normality because different compounds have different capacities to donate hydrogen ions. In a 1 N acid solution consisting of dissolved HCl, the molarity of HCl is 1 M, because HCl is a monoprotic acid, but if the dissolved acid is H_2SO_4, then the molarity of H_2SO_4 in a 1 N acid solution is 0.5 M, because H_2SO_4 is a diprotic acid. The conversion from normality of acid solution to molarity of acidic compound is:

Molarity = Normality/n

where n is the number of protons, hydroxide ions, electrons, or monovalent ions "produced" or "consumed" per molecule of the compound in the reaction.

There is a real benefit to working with equivalents and normality because it allows a direct comparison of quantities of the "thing" you are most interested in. Face it, in an acid-base reaction you really only care about the hydrogen ion and/or the hydroxide ion. Where they come from is not really your primary concern. So, it is very convenient to be able to say that one equivalent of acid (hydrogen ion) will neutralize one equivalent of base (hydroxide ion). The same could not be said to be necessarily true if we were dealing with moles of acidic compound and moles of basic compound. For example, one mole of HCl will not completely neutralize one mole of $Ca(OH)_2$, because one mole of HCl will donate one equivalent of acid, but $Ca(OH)_2$ will donate two equivalents of base.

Conceptually, that was the most challenging discussion in this chapter. Let's move on to review ways in which compounds are represented.

Representation of Compounds ★★★☆☆

There are different ways of representing compounds and their constituent atoms. We've already reviewed a couple of these systems (Lewis dot structures and VSEPR theory) in Chapter 3. In organic chemistry, it is common to encounter "skeletal" representations of compounds, called structural formulas, to show the various bonds between the constituent atoms of a compound. Inorganic chemistry typically represents compounds by showing the constituent atoms without representing the actual bond connectivity or atomic arrangement. For example, $C_6H_{12}O_6$ (which you ought to recognize is the molecular formula for glucose) tells us that this particular compound consists of six atoms of carbon, 12 atoms of hydrogen, and six atoms of oxygen, but there is no indication in the molecular formula of how the different atoms are arranged or how many bonds exist between each of the atoms.

LAW OF CONSTANT COMPOSITION

The **law of constant composition** states that any pure sample of a given compound will contain the same elements in the identical mass ratio. For example, every sample of H_2O will contain two hydrogen atoms for every one oxygen atom or, in terms of mass, for every one gram of hydrogen there will be eight grams of oxygen. We're sorry to say that it doesn't matter whether the water you drink is sourced from deep springs in the Fiji Islands or flows out of a tap connected to a shallow well. The law of constant composition says that water is water.

EMPIRICAL AND MOLECULAR FORMULAS

There are two ways to express a formula—the elemental composition—for a compound. The **empirical formula** gives the simplest whole number ratio of the elements in the compound. The **molecular formula** gives the exact number of atoms of each element in the compound, and is usually a multiple of the empirical formula. For example, the empirical formula for benzene is CH, while the molecular formula is C_6H_6. For some compounds, the empirical and molecular formulas are the same, as in the case of H_2O. For the reasons previously discussed, ionic compounds, such as NaCl or $CaCO_3$, will only have empirical formulas.

PERCENT COMPOSITION

The **percent composition by mass** of an element is the weight percent of a given element in a specific compound. To determine the percent composition of an element X in a compound, the following formula is used:

% Composition = (Mass of X in Formula/Formula Weight of Compound) × 100%

You can calculate the percent composition of an element by using either the empirical or the molecular formula; just be sure to use to the appropriate mass measurement:

MCAT Expertise

Percent composition is a common way for stoichiometry to be tested on the MCAT. Practice these problems to build up speed and efficiency for Test Day.

formula weight for empirical formula or molar mass for molecular formula. Formula weight is simply the mass of the atoms in the empirical formula of a compound.

You can determine the molecular formula if both the percent compositions and molar mass of the compound are known. The following examples demonstrate such calculations.

MCAT Expertise

When there are two methods for approaching a problem, be well-versed in both. Knowing multiple ways to solve a problem will help you tackle questions efficiently.

Example: What is the percent composition of chromium in $K_2Cr_2O_7$?

Solution: The formula weight of $K_2Cr_2O_7$ is:

$$2(39 \text{ g/mol}) + 2(52 \text{ g/mol}) + 7(16 \text{ g/mol}) = 294 \text{ g/mol}$$

$$\% \text{ composition of Cr} = \frac{2(52 \text{ g/mol})}{294 \text{ g/mol}} \times 100$$

$$= 0.354 \times 100$$

$$= 35.4 \text{ percent}$$

Example: What are the empirical and molecular formulas of a compound that contains 40.9 percent carbon, 4.58 percent hydrogen, 54.52 percent oxygen, and has a molar mass of 264 g/mol?

Method One: First, determine the number of moles of each element in the compound by assuming a 100-gram sample; this converts the percentage of each element present directly into grams of that element. Then convert grams to moles:

$$\# \text{mol of C} = \frac{40.9 \text{ g}}{12 \text{ g/mol}} = 3.41 \text{ mol}$$

$$\# \text{mol of H} = \frac{4.58 \text{ g}}{1 \text{ g/mol}} = 4.58 \text{ mol}$$

$$\# \text{mol of O} = \frac{54.52 \text{ g}}{16 \text{ g/mol}} = 3.41 \text{ mol}$$

Next, find the simplest whole number ratio of the elements by dividing the number of moles by the smallest number obtained in the previous step.

$$C : \frac{3.41}{3.41} = 1.00 \qquad H : \frac{4.58}{3.41} = 1.33 \qquad O : \frac{3.41}{3.41} = 1.00$$

Finally, the empirical formula is obtained by converting the numbers obtained into whole numbers (multiplying them by an integer value).

$$C_1 H_{1.33} O_1 \times 3 = C_3 H_4 O_3$$

$C_3H_4O_3$ is the empirical formula. To determine the molecular formula, divide the molar mass by the formula weight. The resultant value is the number of empirical formula units in the molecular formula.

The empirical formula weight of $C_3H_4O_3$ is:

$$3(12 \text{ g/mol}) + 4(1 \text{ g/mol}) + 3(16 \text{ g/mol}) = 88 \text{ g/mol}$$

$$\frac{264 \text{ g/mol}}{88 \text{ g/mol}} = 3$$

$C_3H_4O_3 \times 3 = C_9H_{12}O_9$ is the molecular formula.

Method Two: When the molar mass is given, it is generally easier to find the molecular formula first. This is accomplished by multiplying the molar mass by the given percentages to find the grams of each element present in one mole of compound, then dividing by the respective atomic weights to find the mole ratio of the elements:

$$\text{\# mol of C} = \frac{(0.409)(264) \text{ g}}{12 \text{ g/mol}} = 9 \text{ mol}$$

$$\text{\# mol of H} = \frac{(0.458)(264) \text{ g}}{1 \text{ g/mol}} = 12 \text{ mol}$$

$$\text{\# mol of O} = \frac{(0.5452)(264) \text{ g}}{16 \text{ g/mol}} = 9 \text{ mol}$$

Thus the molecular formula, $C_9H_{12}O_9$, is the direct result.

The empirical formula can now be found by reducing the subscript ratio to the simplest integral values.

Key Concept

The molecular formula is either the same as the empirical formula or a multiple of it. To calculate the molecular formula, you need to know the mole ratio (this will give you the empirical formula) and the molecular weight (molecular weight ÷ empirical formula weight will give you the multiplier for the empirical formula to molecular formula conversion).

Types of Chemical Reactions ★★★☆☆

This section reviews the major classes of chemical reactions. As it has probably already become apparent to you in your inorganic and organic chemistry classes, it would be quite impossible to memorize every single individual reaction that could occur. Fortunately, there is no need to memorize any reaction, as long as you take the time now and throughout your preparation for the MCAT to learn and understand the recognizable patterns of reactivities between compounds. Some classes of compounds react in very "stereotyped" ways or at least appear to react in stereotyped ways because of the MCAT's focus on a particular subset of a chemical's reactivities. The MCAT has a tendency to typecast certain compounds, in spite of repeated protests made by the compounds' talent agents.

COMBINATION REACTIONS

A **combination reaction** has two or more reactants forming one product. The formation of sulfur dioxide by burning sulfur in air is an example of a combination reaction.

$$S\ (s) + O_2\ (g) \rightarrow SO_2\ (g)$$

Key Concept

Combination reactions generally have more reactants than products.

$A + B \rightarrow C$

13. B

What you are shown is a net ionic equation. To answer this question, work backward from the amount of product to the reactant with its spectator ions (in this case, sulfate).

First, for every two moles of FeSCN we create, we must react two moles of Fe^{3+}. Therefore, you're looking for the mass of iron sulfate that can provide two moles of iron.

Next, determine the charge on sulfate, which is -2 and iron, which in this case is +3. Therefore, iron sulfate must be present as:

$$Fe_2(SO_4)_3$$

The molecular formula tells you that each mole of iron sulfate releases two moles of atomic iron. Therefore, you only need one mole of iron sulfate for this reaction, which means the molar mass of iron sulfate is the answer.

$$2 \text{ Fe: } (2)(55.8 \text{ g})$$
$$3 \text{ S: } (3)(32.1 \text{ g})$$
$$\underline{12 \text{ O: } (12)(16.0 \text{ g})}$$
$$399.9 \text{ g}$$

5

Chemical Kinetics
and Equilibrium

It's Friday night, and you're on the first call of your pediatrics rotation. You're a third-year medical student now, and you're anxious to see some action. Hanging out in the call room near the ED of the children's hospital, you get a page from the resident: *Come to the emergency room, now*, she says, *they just brought in a kid with DKA*. DKA, you know, stands for diabetic ketoacidosis and is a fairly common way for undiagnosed Type I diabetes to present. Entering the child's room, the examination is already under way; he's young—about 10 years old—conscious but agitated, and the most obvious sign, what you notice immediately, is his rapid, shallow breathing. You see he's already receiving IV fluids and an insulin drip.

Later that evening, after the boy has stabilized, you and the resident are talking about diabetes and DKA. You remembered from your second-year lessons about endocrine pathophysiology that ketoacidosis can arise as a result of the body's metabolism of fatty acids when insulin production finally shuts down in Type I diabetes. Because most of the cells of the human body can't import glucose without the aid of insulin, the glucose accumulates in the plasma of the blood, producing hyperglycemia even as the cells of the body are in a state of glucose starvation. Fatty acids are metabolized into ketone bodies as an alternative energy source. Some of the ketones produced are ketoacids and as the diabetic crisis continues and worsens, the concentration of these ketoacids increases, resulting in a plasma pH below 7.35 (metabolic acidosis). The combination of the acidosis, progressively severe dehydration due to the osmotic effect of glucose "spilling into" the urine, and other negative effects of the severe insulin depletion, results in the host of signs and symptoms of diabetic ketoacidosis. You ask the resident why the boy was hyperventilating, and she takes a piece of paper and writes out the following:

$$H^+ (aq) + HCO_3^- (aq) \rightarrow H_2CO_3 (aq) \rightarrow CO_2 (g) + H_2O (l)$$

It's Le Châtelier's principle, she deadpans, disappointed that you didn't remember that. *The respiratory system is trying to compensate for the metabolic acidosis; the increased breathing rate allows the patient to blow off more CO_2, which causes the equilibrium to shift to the right. Hydrogen ions combine with bicarbonate ions to produce carbonic acid, which dissociates into CO_2 gas to replace the gas that's being expelled from the lungs. Of course, the desired result is a decrease in the hydrogen ion concentration, which stabilizes the pH and keeps it from getting crazy low. It's not perfect, but if you catch them soon enough, the pH hasn't gone so low that they've essentially become a scrambled egg. You should know all of this by now.*

You recognize the equation. In fact, you even remember studying it for your MCAT. *What was that all about? Oh yeah, chemical equilibrium. Wow, chemistry really is essential for medical school!*

This chapter focuses on two primary topics: chemical kinetics and chemical equilibrium. As the term suggests, chemical kinetics is the study of reaction rates, the effects of reaction conditions on these rates, and the mechanisms implied by such observations. Chemical equilibrium is a dynamic state of a chemical reaction at which the concentrations of reactants and products stabilize over time in a low energy configuration. Pay particular attention to the concepts of chemical equilibrium, as we will return to them in our review of solutions, acid-base, and redox chemistry.

Chemical Kinetics

Reactions can be spontaneous or nonspontaneous; the change in Gibbs free energy determines whether or not a reaction will occur, by itself, without outside assistance (see Chapter 6, Thermochemistry). However, even if a reaction is spontaneous, this does not necessarily mean that it will run quickly. In fact, nearly every reaction that our very lives depend upon, while perhaps spontaneous, proceed so slowly that without the aid of enzymes and other catalysts we might not ever actually "see" the reaction occur over the course of an average human lifetime. In biology, we discuss the function of enzymes, which selectively enhance the rate of certain reactions (by a factor of 10^6 to 10^{14}) over other thermodynamically feasible reaction pathways, thereby determining the course of cellular metabolism, the collection of all chemical reactions in a living cell. For now, however, let us review the topics of reaction mechanisms, rates, rate laws and the factors that affect them.

REACTION MECHANISMS

Very rarely is the balanced reaction equation, with which we work to calculate limiting reactants and yields, an accurate representation of the actual steps involved in the chemical process from reactants to products. Many reactions proceed by more than one step, the series of which is known as the **mechanism** of a reaction, and the sum of which gives the **overall reaction** (the one that you, typically, are asked to balance). When you know the accepted mechanism of a reaction, this helps you explain the reaction's rate, position of equilibrium, and thermodynamic characteristics (see Chapter 6). Consider the generic reaction:

Overall reaction: $A_2 + 2B \rightarrow 2AB$

On its own, this equation seems to imply a mechanism in which two molecules of B collide with one molecule of A_2 to form two molecules of AB. Suppose instead, however, that the reaction actually takes place in two steps:

Step 1: $A_2 + B \rightarrow A_2B$ (slow)

Step 2: $A_2B + B \rightarrow 2AB$ (fast)

You'll note that the two steps, taken together, give the overall (net) reaction. The molecule A_2B, which does not appear in the overall reaction, is called an **intermediate.** Reaction intermediates are often difficult to detect because they may be consumed almost immediately after they are formed, but a proposed mechanism that includes

Bridge

Mechanisms are proposed pathways for a reaction that must coincide with rate data information from experimental observation. We will be studying mechanisms more in Organic Chemistry.

intermediates can be supported through kinetic experiments. One of the most important points for you to remember is that the slowest step in any proposed mechanism is called the rate-determining step, because it acts like a kinetic "bottleneck," preventing the overall reaction from proceeding any faster than the slowest step. It holds up the entire process in much the same way that the overall rate of an assembly line production can only be as fast as the slowest step or slowest person (who will probably soon find himself reassigned to a desk job).

Reaction Rates ★★★★☆

Reactions, unfortunately, do not come with handy built-in speedometers. We can't just look at a dial or gauge and read the reaction rate. It takes a little more effort than that. To determine the rate at which a reaction proceeds we must take measurements of concentrations of reactants and products and note their change over time.

DEFINITION OF RATE

If we consider a generic reaction, $2A + B \rightarrow C$, in which one mole of C is produced from every two moles of A and one mole of B, we can describe the rate of this reaction in terms of either the disappearance of reactants over time or the appearance of products over time. Because the reactants, by definition, are being consumed in the process of formation of the products, we place a minus sign in front of the rate expression in terms of reactants. For the previous reaction, the rate of the reaction with respect to A is $-\Delta[A]/\Delta t$, with respect to B is $-\Delta[B]/\Delta t$, and with respect to C is $\Delta[C]/\Delta t$. You'll notice that the stoichiometric coefficients for the reaction are not equal, and this tells you that the rates of change of concentrations are not equal. Because two moles of A are consumed for every mole of B consumed, $\text{rate}_{-\Delta[A]} = 2\,\text{rate}_{-\Delta[B]}$. Furthermore, for every two moles of A consumed, only one mole of C is produced; thus we can say that the rate $_{-\Delta[A]} = 2\,\text{rate}_{\Delta[C]}$. Based on the stoichoimetry, you can see that the rate of consumption of B is equal to the rate of production of C. To show a standard rate of reaction in which the rates with respect to all reaction species are equal, the rate of concentration change of each species should be divided by the species' stoichiometric coefficient:

$$\text{rate} = \frac{-1\Delta[A]}{2\Delta t} = -\frac{-\Delta[B]}{\Delta t} = \frac{\Delta[C]}{\Delta t},$$

and for the general reaction $aA + bB \rightarrow cC + dD$:

$$\frac{-1\Delta[A]}{a\,\Delta t} = -\frac{-1\Delta[B]}{b\Delta t} = \frac{-1\Delta[C]}{c\Delta t} = \frac{-1\Delta[D]}{d\,\Delta t}$$

Rate is expressed in the units of moles per liter per second (mol/L/s) or molarity per second (M/s).

DETERMINATION OF RATE LAW

Here's something you can take to the bank (that is, to the MCAT testing center): In the Physical Sciences section of the MCAT, it is extremely unlikely that the test maker will give you a reaction equation that you can merely look at and write the correct rate law. Therefore, on the MCAT, whenever you are asked to determine the rate law for a reaction in which you are given the net equation, the first thing you will do is look for experimental data.

However, we're getting ahead of ourselves, so let's start with the basics. For nearly all forward, irreversible reactions, the rate is proportional to the product of the concentrations of the reactants, each raised to some power. For the general reaction:

$$aA + bB \rightarrow cC + dD$$

the rate is proportional to $[A]^x[B]^y$. By including a proportionality constant, k, we can say that rate is determined according to the following equation:

$$\text{rate} = k[A]^x[B]^y$$

This expression is called the **rate law** for the general reaction shown here, where k is the reaction rate coefficient or rate constant. Rate is always measured in units of concentration over time, that is, molarity/second. The exponents x and y (or x, y, and z, if there are three reactants, etc.) are called the orders of the reaction: x is the order with respect to reactant A, and y is order with respect to reactant B. The overall order of the reaction is the sum of $x + y$ ($+ z...$). These exponents may be integers, fractions, or zero and must be determined experimentally. The MCAT will focus almost entirely on zero, first, second, and third order reactions only. Furthermore, in most cases, the exponents will be integers.

Before we go any further in our consideration of rate laws, we must offer a few warnings about common traps that students often fall into. The first—and most common—is the mistaken assumption that the orders of a reaction are the same as the stoichiometric coefficients in the balanced overall equation. Pay close attention to this: *the values of x and y usually aren't the same as the stoichiometric coefficients.* The orders of a reaction are usually must be determined experimentally. There are only two cases in which you can take stoichiometric coefficients as the orders of reaction. The first is when the reaction mechanism is a single step and the balanced "overall" reaction is reflective of the entire chemical process. The second is when the complete reaction mechanism is given and the rate-determining step is indicated. The stoichiometric coefficients on the reactant side of the rate-determining step are the orders of the reaction. Occasionally, even this can get a little complicated when the rate-determining step involves an intermediate as a reactant, in which case you must derive the intermediate molecule's concentration by the law of mass action (that is, the equilibrium constant expression) for the step that produced it.

The second trap to be wary of is mistaking the equilibrium aspect of the law of mass action for the kinetic aspect. The equations for the two aspects do look similar and if you're not alert, you may mistake one for the other or use one when you should

Mixed-Order Reactions

Mixed-order reactions sometimes refer to noninteger orders (fractions), and in other cases to reactions whose order varies over the course of the reaction. Fractions are more specifically described as broken-order, and in recent times, the term *mixed-order* has come to refer solely to reactions whose order changes over time. Knowing those two definitions will probably be enough for you on Test Day.

An example of a mixed-order reaction is a catalyzed reaction whose rate law is given by

$$\text{Rate} = \frac{k_1[E][A]^2}{k_2 + k_3[A]},$$

where A is the single reactant and E the catalyst. (The overall reaction and its mechanism are beyond the relevance and scope of the MCAT, and the derivation of this rate law is even more unnecessary!) The result of the large value for [A] at the beginning of the reaction is that $k_3[A] \gg k_2$, and the reaction will appear to be first-order; at the end of the reaction $k_2 \gg k_3[A]$ because [A] will have a low value, making the reaction appear to be second-order. While the MCAT will not ask you to derive a rate expression for a mixed-order reaction, you are responsible for being able to recognize how the rate order changes as the specific reactant concentration changes.

THEORIES OF THE MOLECULAR BASIS OF CHEMICAL REACTIONS

It's one thing to say "A_2 reacts with B_2 to form 2AB"; it's quite another to be able to describe, as precisely as possible, the actual interactions that occur between A_2 and B_2 to produce AB at some rate. Various theories have been proposed to explain the events that are taking place at the atomic level through the process of a reaction.

Collision Theory of Chemical Kinetics

In order for a reaction to occur, molecules must collide with each other, in much the same way that in order for children to enjoy themselves, there usually must be some rough physical contact involved, that is, of course, until someone's eye gets poked out. The **collision theory of chemical kinetics** states that the rate of a reaction is proportional to the number of collisions per second between the reacting molecules.

The theory suggests, however, that not all collisions result in a chemical reaction. An effective collision (that is, one that leads to the formation of products) occurs only if the molecules collide with each other in correct orientation and sufficient energy to break the existing bonds and form new ones. Not every punch that a professional boxer throws is going to result in a knockout, only the ones that have the right angle and energy. The minimum energy of collision necessary for a reaction to take place is called the **activation energy**, E_a, or the **energy barrier**. Only a fraction of colliding particles have enough kinetic energy to exceed the activation energy. This means that only a fraction of all collisions are effective. The rate of a reaction can therefore be expressed as:

$$rate = fZ$$

where Z is the total number of collisions occurring per second and f is the fraction of collisions that are effective.

Transition State Theory

The discussion of this theory introduces us to some terms that will be more fully defined and explored in the next chapter, Thermochemistry, so if some of these concepts are not clear to you, be patient, because you'll have another opportunity to consider them more carefully soon enough.

When molecules collide with sufficient energy at least equal to the activation energy, they form a **transition state,** in which the old bonds are weakened and the new bonds begin to form. The transition state then dissociates into products and the new bonds are fully formed. For the reaction $A_2 + B_2 = 2AB$, the change along the reaction coordinate, which is a measure of the extent to which the reaction has progressed from reactants to products (see Figures 5.1 and 5.2), can be represented as follows:

Figure 5.1

Key Concept

Relative to reactants and products, transition states have the highest energy. So, they are only theoretical structures and cannot be isolated. Nevertheless, we can still use the proposed structures to better understand the reactions in which they are involved.

The **transition state,** also called the **activated complex,** has greater energy than either the reactants or the products, and is denoted by the symbol ‡. An amount of energy at least equal to the activation energy is required to bring the reactants to this energy level. Once an activated complex is formed, it can either dissociate into the products or revert to reactants without any additional energy input. Transition states are distinguished from reaction intermediates in that, existing as they do at energy maxima, transition states exist on a continuum rather than having distinct identities and finite lifetimes.

A potential energy diagram illustrates the relationship between the activation energy, the heats of reaction, and the potential energy of the system. The most important features to recognize in such diagrams are the relative energies of all of the products and reactants. The **enthalpy change of the reaction (ΔH)**

is the difference between the potential energy of the products and the potential energy of the reactants (see Chapter 6). A negative enthalpy change indicates an **exothermic reaction** (one in which heat is given off) and a positive enthalpy indicates an **endothermic reaction** (one in which heat is absorbed). The activated complex, the transition state, exists at the top of the energy barrier. The difference in potential energies between the activated complex and the reactants is the activation energy of the forward reaction; the difference potential in energies between the activated complex and the products is the activation energy of the reverse reaction.

For example, consider the formation of HCl from H_2 and Cl_2. The overall reaction is:

$$H_2 (g) + Cl_2 (g) \leftrightarrow 2HCl (g)$$

Figure 5.2 shows that the reaction is exothermic. The potential energy of the products is less than the potential energy of the reactants; heat is evolved and the enthalpy change of the reaction is negative.

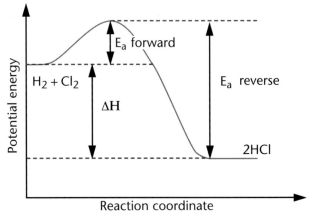

Figure 5.2

Key Concept

$-\Delta H$ = exothermic = heat given off

$+\Delta H$ = endothermic = heat absorbed

MCAT Expertise

Kinetics and thermodynamics should be considered separately. Note that the potential energy of the product can be raised or lowered, thereby changing the value of ΔH without affecting the value of forward E_a.

FACTORS AFFECTING REACTION RATE

If you would imagine a group of children playing together in a rough-and-tumble game of tag, we can identify certain conditions that would result in a more vigorous, more fun, more effective game. We can use this analogy to remember the factors that can affect chemical reaction rates.

Reactant Concentrations

A group of children playing tag will probably have more fun the greater the number of children playing: the participation of more children equals more opportunities to chase, trip, and tag each other. The greater the concentrations of the reactants,

MCAT Expertise

We saw earlier in this chapter that increasing reactant concentrations might increase the reaction rate, but be aware of each reactant's order before making this assumption.

the greater the number of effective collisions per unit time, and therefore the reaction rate will increase for all but zero-order reactions. For reactions occurring in the gaseous state, the partial pressures of the gas reactants serve as a measure of concentration (see Chapter 7, The Gas Phase).

Temperature

You can imagine that children's enthusiasm for playing tag outside increases as the temperature warms from the bone-chilling snowstorms of winter to the pleasant sun of June. For nearly all reactions, the reaction rate will increase as the temperature increases. Because the temperature of a substance is a measure of the particles' average kinetic energy, increasing the temperature increases the average kinetic energy of the molecules. Consequently, the proportion of molecules having energies greater than E_a (thus capable of undergoing reaction) increases with higher temperature. You'll oftentimes hear that raising the temperature of a system by 10°C will result in an approximate doubling of the reaction rate. You have to be careful with this approximation as it is *generally* true for biological systems but not so for many other systems. (Don't forget also: if the temperature gets too high, a catalyst may denature—and then the reaction rate plummets!)

Medium

The rate at which a reaction takes place may also be affected by the medium in which it takes place. Just as children playing tag would prefer to play on a grassy field, but another group of children wanting to get a game of ice hockey going would be looking for an ice rink, some molecules are more likely to react with each other in aqueous environments, while others are more likely to react in a nonaqueous solvent such as DMSO (dimethylsulfoxide) or ethanol. Furthermore, the physical state of the medium (liquid, solid, or gas) can also have a significant effect. Generally polar solvents are preferred because their molecular dipole tends to polarize the bonds of the reactants, thereby lengthening and weakening them, which permits the reaction to occur faster.

Catalysts

Catalysts are substances that increase reaction rate without themselves being consumed in the reaction. Catalysts interact with the reactants, either by adsorption or through the formation of intermediates, and stabilize them so as to reduce the energy of activation necessary for the reaction to proceed. While many catalysts, including all enzymes, chemically interact with the reactants, upon formation of the products, they return to their original chemical state. They may increase the frequency of collisions between the reactants, change the relative orientation of the reactants making a higher percentage of the collisions effective, donate electron density to the reactants, or reduce intramolecular bonding within reactant molecules. In **homogeneous catalysis,** the catalyst is in the same phase (solid, liquid, gas) as the reactants. In **heterogeneous catalysis,** the catalyst is in a distinct phase. Figure 5.3 compares the energy profiles of catalyzed and uncatalyzed reactions.

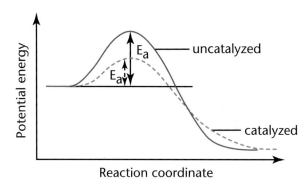

Figure 5.3

If you look closely at the energy profiles in the figure, you'll notice that the only effect of the catalyst is the decrease in the energies of activation, E_a, for both the forward and reverse reactions. The presence of the catalyst has no impact on the potential energies of the reactants or the products or the difference between them. This means that catalysts change only the rate of reactions, and in fact, they change the forward rate and the reverse rate by the same factor. Consequently, they have no impact whatsoever on the equilibrium position or the measure of K_{eq}. Of course, you have to remember that as useful as catalysts are in biological and nonbiological systems, catalysts are not miracle workers: they will not transform a nonspontaneous reaction into a spontaneous one; they only make spontaneous reactions go more quickly toward equilibrium.

Equilibrium ★★★★★★

We've been dancing around this term for the past couple of pages now. We warned you not to confuse the chemical equilibrium expression for the rate expression. We stressed that catalysts make reactions go faster toward their equilibrium position, but that they can't actually change the equilibrium position or alter the value of K_{eq}. Well, now we're really going to get into it—and you'd better start paying attention because the principles and concepts that are the focus of the rest of this chapter will direct our discussion in the upcoming chapters about some of the most important general chemistry topics for the MCAT: solutions, acids and bases, and redox reactions.

DYNAMIC EQUILIBRIUM OF REVERSIBLE CHEMICAL REACTIONS

So far, in our discussion of reaction rates, we have been assuming that the reactions were **irreversible,** that is, the reaction proceeds in one direction only, the reaction goes to completion, and the amount of product formed is the maximum as determined by the amount of limiting reactant present. **Reversible reactions** are those in which the reaction can proceed in one of two ways: forward and reverse. (From the perspective of the direction in which the overall reaction is written, the forward reaction is the one that goes from "reactants" on the left to "products" on the right.) Reversible reactions usually do not proceed to completion because (by definition) the products can react together to re-form the reactants. When the reaction system is closed and no products or reactants are removed or added, the system will eventually "settle" into a state in which the rate of the forward reaction equals the rate of the reverse reaction and the concentrations of the products and reactants are constant. In this **dynamic equilibrium** state, the forward and reverse reactions are occurring—they haven't stopped, as would be the case in a static equilibrium—but they are going at the same rate, thus there is no net change in the concentrations of the products or reactants. Consider the following generic reversible reaction:

$$A \leftrightarrow B$$

At equilibrium, the concentrations of A and B are constant (though not necessarily equal), and the reactions $A \rightarrow B$ and $B \rightarrow A$ continue to occur at equal rates.

Equilibrium can be thought of as a balance between the two reactions (forward and reverse). Better still, equilibrium should be understood on the basis of entropy, which is the measure of the distribution of energy throughout a system or between a system and its environment. For a reversible reaction at a given temperature, the reaction will reach equilibrium when the system's entropy—or energy distribution—is at a maximum, and the Gibbs free energy of the system is at a minimum.

LAW OF MASS ACTION

For a generic reversible reaction $aA + bB \rightarrow cC + dD$, the **law of mass action** states that if the system is at equilibrium at a given temperature, then the following ratio is constant:

$$K_{eq} = \frac{[C]^c [D]^d}{[A]^a [B]^b}$$

The law of mass action is actually related to the expressions for the rates of the forward and reverse reactions. Consider the following one-step reversible reaction:

$$2A \leftrightarrow B + C$$

Because the reaction occurs in one step, the rates of the forward and reverse reactions are given by:

$$\text{rate}_f = k_f[A]^2, \text{ and rate}_r = k_r[B][C]$$

When $\text{rate}_f = \text{rate}_r$, the system is in equilibrium. Because the rates are equal, we can set the rate expressions for the forward and reverse reactions equal to each other:

$$k_f[A]^2 = k_r[B][C] \text{ and } \frac{k_f}{k_r} = \frac{[B][C]}{[A]^2}$$

Because k_f and k_r are both constants, we can define a new constant K_c, where K_c is called the equilibrium constant, and the subscript c indicates that it is in terms of concentration (when dealing with gases, the equilibrium constant is referred to a K_p and the subscript p indicates that it is in terms of pressure). For dilute solutions K_c and K_{eq} are used interchangeably. The new equation can thus be written:

$$K_c = K_{eq} = \frac{[B][C]}{[A]^2}$$

While the forward and the reverse reaction rates are equal at equilibrium, the concentrations of the reactants and products are not usually equal. This means that the forward and reverse reaction rate constants, k_f and k_r, are not usually equal. The ratio of k_f to k_r is K_c (K_{eq}).

$$\frac{k_f}{k_r} = K_c = K_{eq}$$

When a reaction occurs by more than one step, the equilibrium constant for the overall reaction is found by multiplying together the equilibrium constants for each step of the reaction. When you do this, the equilibrium constant for the overall reaction is equal to the concentrations of the products divided by the concentrations of the reactants in the overall reaction, each concentration term raised to the stoichiometric coefficient for the respective species. The forward and reverse rate constants for the nth step are designated k_n and k_{-n}, respectively. For example, if the reaction

$$aA + bB \rightarrow cC + dD$$

occurs in three steps, then

$$K_c = \frac{k_1 k_2 k_3}{k_{-1} k_{-2} k_{-3}} = \frac{[C]^c [D]^d}{[A]^a [B]^b}.$$

> **Example:** What is the expression for the equilibrium constant for the following reaction?
>
> $$3\,H_2\,(g) + N_2\,(g) \rightleftarrows 2\,NH_3\,(g)$$
>
> **Solution:** $K_c = \dfrac{[NH_3]^2}{[H_2]^3 [N_2]}$

REACTION QUOTIENT

The law of mass action defines the position of equilibrium by stating that the ratio of the product of the concentrations of the products, each raised to their respective stoichiometric coefficients, to the product of the concentrations of the reactants, each raised to their respective stoichiometric coefficients, is constant. However, equilibrium is a state that is achieved only through time. Depending on the actual rates

Key Concept

For most purposes, you will not need to distinguish between different K values. For dilute solutions, $K_{eq} \approx K_c$ and both are calculated in units of concentration.

MCAT Expertise

Remember our earlier warning about confusion between reaction coefficients and rate laws? Well, here the coefficients *are* equal to the exponents in the equilibrium expression. On Test Day, if the reaction is balanced then the equilibrium expression should just about write itself on your scratch paper.

of the forward and reverse reactions, equilibrium might be achieved in minutes or years. What can we use as a kind of "timer" that tells us how far along in the process toward equilibrium the reaction has reached? We can take another measurement of concentrations, called the reaction quotient, Q_c. At any point in time of a reaction, we can measure the concentrations of all the reactants and products and calculate the reaction quotient according to the following equation

$$Q_c = \frac{[C]^c[D]^d}{[A]^a[B]^b}$$

You should be struck by how similar this looks to the equation for K_{eq}. It's the same form, but the information it provides is quite different. While the concentrations used for the law of mass action are equilibrium (constant) concentrations, when calculating a value of Q_c for a reaction, the concentrations of the reactants and products may not be constant. In fact, if Q_c changes over time because the concentrations of reaction species are changing, the reaction by definition is not at the equilibrium state. Thus, the utility of Q_c is not the value itself, but the comparison that can be made of the calculated Q_c at any given moment in time of the reaction to the known K_{eq} for the reaction at a given temperature. For any reaction, if:

- $Q_c < K_{eq}$, then the reaction has not yet reached equilibrium.
- $Q_c > K_{eq}$, then the reaction has exceeded equilibrium.
- $Q_c = K_{eq}$, then the reaction is in dynamic equilibrium.

Any reaction that has not yet reached the equilibrium state, as indicated $Q_c < K_{eq}$, will continue spontaneously in the forward direction (that is, consuming reactants to form products) until the equilibrium ratio of reactants and products is reached. Any reaction in the equilibrium state will continue to react in the forward and reverse direction but the reaction rates for the forward and reverse reactions will be equal and the concentrations of the reactants and products will be constant, such that $Q_c = K_{eq}$. Once a reaction is at equilibrium any further "movement" either in the forward direction (resulting in an increase in products) or in the reverse direction (resulting in the re-formation of reactants) will be nonspontaneous. In Chapter 6, Thermochemistry, we'll review methods of introducing changes in systems at equilibrium and discuss how those systems respond in terms of enthalpy, spontaneity, and entropy.

PROPERTIES OF THE LAW OF MASS ACTION

Remember the following characteristics of the law of mass action and the equilibrium constant expression:

- The concentrations of pure solids and pure liquids (the solvent, really) do not appear in the equilibrium constant expression because for the purposes of the MCAT, their concentrations do not change in the course of the reaction. (Actually, the concentrations of any pure solids and/or pure liquids are included in the expression, but we assign them a value of 1, and "hide" the actual concentrations by incorporating them into the equilibrium constant.

- K_{eq} is characteristic of a particular reaction at a given temperature: the equilibrium constant is temperature-dependent.
- Generally, the larger the value for K_{eq}, the farther to the right that we'll find the equilibrium and the more complete the reaction.
- If the equilibrium constant for a reaction written in one direction is K_{eq}, the equilibrium constant for the reaction written in reverse is $1/K_{eq}$.

Le Châtelier's Principle ★★★★☆

We can think of few other examples of a scientist's legacy being so tarnished by such rampant mispronunciation of her or his name. While we can all be thankful that the MCAT is not an oral examination with penalties for mispronunciation, let's just clear it up once and for all: dear Henry Louis's surname is pronounced lə′shäd·əl′ya. The principle that bears his name, and for which he is most famous, states that a system to which a "stress" is applied tends to shift so as to relieve the applied stress. No matter what the particular form the stress takes (e.g., change in concentration of one component or another, change in pressure, or change in temperature), the effect of the stress is to cause the reaction to move temporarily out of its equilibrium state, either because the concentrations or partial pressures of the system are no longer in the equilibrium ratio, or because the equilibrium ratio has actually changed as a result of a change in the temperature of the system. The reaction then responds by reacting in whichever direction (that is, either forward or reverse) that results in a reestablishment of the equilibrium state.

> **MCAT Expertise**
>
> Le Châtelier's principle applies to a wide variety of systems and as such, appears as a fundamental concept in both MCAT science sections.

CHANGES IN CONCENTRATION OF A REACTANT SPECIES

When you add or remove reactants or products from a reaction in equilibrium, you are causing the reaction to no longer be at its energy minimum state. Metaphorically, you have pushed the reaction, like a ball, up a little ways along the slope of the energy hills on either side of the energy valley. The actual effect is that with the change in concentration of one or another of the chemical species, you have caused the system to have a ratio of products to reactants that is not equal to the equilibrium ratio. In other words, changing the concentration of either a reactant or a product results in $Q_c \neq K_{eq}$. By adding reactant or removing product, you have created a situation in which $Q_c < K_{eq}$, and the reaction will spontaneously react in the forward direction, increasing the value of Q_c until $Q_c = K_{eq}$. By removing reactant or adding product, you have created a situation in which $Q_c > K_{eq}$, and the reaction will spontaneously react in the reverse direction, thereby decreasing the value of Q_c until once again $Q_c = K_{eq}$. A simple way to remember this is: the system will always react in the direction away from the added species or toward the removed species.

Bridge

Remember the equation:

$$CO_2 + H_2O \rightarrow HCO_3^- + H^+$$

In the tissues, there is a lot of CO_2 and the reaction shifts to the right. In the lungs, CO_2 is lost and the reaction shifts to the left. Note that blowing off CO_2 (hyperventilation) is used as a mechanism of dealing with acidosis (excess H^+).

We often take advantage of this particular tendency of chemical reactions in order to improve the yield of chemical reactions. For example, where possible in the industrial production of chemicals, products of reversible reactions are removed as they are formed so as to prevent the reactions from ever reaching their equilibrium states. The reaction will continue to go in the forward direction, producing more and more product (assuming continual replenishment of reactants as they are consumed in the reaction). You could also drive a reaction forward by starting with higher concentrations of reactants. This will lead to an increase in the absolute quantities of products formed, but the reaction would still eventually reach its equilibrium state, unless product was removed as it formed.

CHANGES IN PRESSURE (BY CHANGING VOLUME)

Because liquids and solids are essentially incompressible, only chemical reactions that involve at least one gas species will be affected by changes to the system's volume and pressure. When you compress a system, its volume decreases and the total pressure increases. The increase in the total pressure is associated with an increase in the partial pressures of all the gases in the system and this results in the system no longer being in the equilibrium state such that $Q_p \neq K_{eq}$. The system will react either forward or reverse, but always toward whichever side has the lower total number of moles of gas. This result is a consequence of the ideal gas law, which tells us that there is a direct relationship between the number of moles of gas and the pressure of the gas. If you increase the pressure on a system, it will respond by decreasing the pressure by means of decreasing the number of gas moles present. (In this case, the volume of the system was decreased *and then held constant* while the system returned to its equilibrium state.) When you expand a system, its volume increases, and the total pressure and partial pressures decrease. The system is no longer in its equilibrium state and will react in the direction of the side with the greater number of moles of gas.

Consider the following reaction:

$$N_2 (g) + 3H_2 \leftrightarrow 2NH_3 (g)$$

The left side of the reaction has a total of four moles of gas molecules, whereas the right side has only two moles. When the pressure of this system is increased, the system will react in the direction that produces fewer moles of gas, in this case, that direction is to the right: more ammonia will form. However, if the pressure is decreased, the system will react in the direction that produces greater moles of gas; the favored reaction will be the reverse: more reactants will re-form.

CHANGE IN TEMPERATURE

Le Châtelier's principle tells us that changing the temperature of a system will also cause the system to react in a particular way so as to "return" to its equilibrium state, but we have to be careful here, because unlike the effect of changing concentrations or pressures, the result of changing temperature is not simply a change in the reaction quotient, Q_c or Q_p, but a change in K_{eq}. The change in temperature doesn't cause the concentrations or partial pressures of the reactants and products to immediately change and so the Q immediately after the temperature change is the same before the temperature change. Before the temperature change, the system was at equilibrium and Q was equal to K_{eq}; now after the temperature change, K_{eq} is a different value (because it depends on temperature) and so $Q \neq K_{eq}$. The system has to react in whichever direction allows it to reach its new equilibrium state at the new temperature. That direction is determined by the enthalpy of the reaction (see Chapter 6, Thermochemistry). You can think of heat as a reactant if the reaction is endothermic ($+\Delta H$) and as a product if the reaction is exothermic ($-\Delta H$). Thinking about heat as a reactant or product allows you to apply the principle that we discussed in regards to concentration changes to temperature changes. For example, consider the following exothermic reaction:

$$A \leftrightarrow B + heat\ (-\Delta H)$$

If we placed this system in an ice bath, its temperature would decrease, driving the reaction to the right to replace the heat lost. Conversely, if the system were placed in a boiling water bath, the reaction would shift to the left due to the increased "concentration" of heat. All of this is to say that on Test Day, when you are asked to predict the direction a reaction would go in response to a change in temperature, you must look for the enthalpy change for the reaction, which will be given somewhere in the passage, figure, or question stem.

Conclusion

We've discussed some very important concepts and principles in this chapter related to the studies of reaction rates and chemical equilibria. We began with a consideration of chemical reactions and the mechanisms that illustrate the possible individual steps necessary to transform reactants into products. We demonstrated the way to derive a reaction's rate law through the analysis of experimental data, and we looked at the factors that can affect the rates of chemical reactions. The second part of this chapter focused on the law of mass action and the significance of the equilibrium state of a chemical reaction. With our understanding of the significance of K_{eq} and Q, we are able to predict the direction that a reaction will go in response to various stresses—concentration, pressure, or temperature changes—that might be applied to a system.

You've worked through another chapter and reviewed some very important topics for Test Day. We cannot stress enough how much all of your hard work and dedication will pay off in points on the MCAT. There's more to learn and review, but you have already made great progress and will continue to do so. Take pride in the work you are doing, and have confidence in yourself and in your preparation with Kaplan.

Key Concept

For the reaction:

$A\ (aq) + 2B\ (g) \leftrightarrow C\ (g) + heat$

Will shift to the right if...	Will shift to the left if...
• A or B added	• C added
• C removed	• A or B removed
• pressure increased or volume reduced	• volume increased or pressure reduced
• temperature reduced	• temperature increased

CONCEPTS TO REMEMBER

☐ Reaction mechanisms propose a series of steps, the sum of which gives the overall reaction that explains the chemical processes in the transformation of reactants into products. The slowest step in a reaction mechanism is the rate-determining step, and it limits the maximum rate at which the reaction can proceed.

☐ Reaction rates can be measured in terms of the rate of disappearance of reactant or the appearance of product, as measured by changes in their respective concentrations.

☐ The generic rate law is rate = $k[A]^x[B]^y$, and a particular reaction's actual rate law usually must be determined by analyzing experimental rate data that relate concentrations of reactants to rates of product formation.

☐ In order for a reaction to occur, molecules of reactants must collide with each other at the proper angle and with an amount of kinetic energy at least as great as the energy maximum of the transition state, known as the energy of activation, E_a.

☐ Reaction rates can be increased by increasing reactant concentrations (except for zero-order reactions), increasing the temperature, changing the medium, or adding a catalyst.

☐ Reversible chemical reactions will eventually "settle" into an energy minimum state (for which there is maximum entropy) called equilibrium. This is a dynamic equilibrium in which the concentrations of reactants and products are constant because the rates of the forward and reverse reactions are equal.

☐ The law of mass action gives the equilibrium constant (K_{eq}) expression. It states that at equilibrium, the ratio of products to reactants will be constant. At equilibrium, the ratio of the forward rate to the reverse rate will be equal to one; however, the ratio of the equilibrium concentrations of products to reactants will usually not be equal to one.

☐ The reaction quotient, Q_c, is a calculated value involving reactant and product concentrations at any time within a reaction. Comparison of the calculated Q_c value to the known K_{eq} value will tell you "where" the reaction is with respect to its equilibrium state.

☐ Pure solids and pure liquids are not included in the law of mass action, and K_{eq} is temperature-dependent.

☐ Le Châtelier's principle states that a chemical system that experiences a stress (changes to concentration, pressure, or temperature) will react in whichever direction results in the reestablishment of the equilibrium state.

EQUATIONS TO REMEMBER

☐   rate = $k[A]^x[B]^y$

☐ $K_{eq} = \dfrac{[C]^c[D]^d}{[A]^a[B]^b}$ at equilibrium

☐ $\dfrac{k_f}{k_r} = K_c = K_{eq}$

☐ $Q_c = \dfrac{[C]^c[D]^d}{[A]^a[B]^b}$

Practice Questions

1. In a third-order reaction involving two reactants and two products, doubling the concentration of the first reactant causes the rate to increase by a factor of 2. What will happen to the rate of this reaction if the concentration of the second reactant is cut in half?

   A. It will increase by a factor of 2.
   B. It will increase by a factor of 4.
   C. It will decrease by a factor of 2.
   D. It will decrease by a factor of 4.

2. In a certain equilibrium process, the activation energy of the forward reaction is greater than the activation energy of the reverse reaction. This reaction is

   A. endothermic.
   B. exothermic.
   C. spontaneous.
   D. nonspontaneous.

3. Carbonated beverages are produced by dissolving carbon dioxide in water to produce carbonic acid

   $$CO_2\ (g) + H_2O\ (l) \rightleftharpoons H_2CO_3\ (aq)$$

   When a bottle containing carbonated water is opened, the taste of the beverage gradually changes until all of the carbonation is lost. Which of the following statements best explains this phenomenon?

   A. The change in pressure and volume causes the reaction to shift to the left, thereby decreasing the amount of aqueous carbonic acid.
   B. The change in pressure and volume causes the reaction to shift to the right, thereby decreasing the amount of gaseous carbon dioxide.
   C. Carbonic acid reacts with environmental oxygen and nitrogen.
   D. Carbon dioxide reacts with environmental oxygen and nitrogen.

4. A certain chemical reaction is endothermic. It occurs spontaneously. Which of the following must be true for this reaction?

   I. $\Delta H > 0$

   II. $\Delta G < 0$

   III. $\Delta S > 0$

   A. I only
   B. I and II only
   C. II and III only
   D. I, II, and III

5. A certain ionic salt, A_3B, has a molar solubility of 10 M at a certain temperature. What is the K_{sp} of this salt at the same temperature?

A. 10^4
B. 3×10^4
C. 2.7×10^5
D. 8.1×10^5

6. Acetic acid dissociates in solution according to the following equation:

$$CH_3COOH \rightleftharpoons CH_3COO^- + H^+$$

If sodium acetate is added to a solution of acetic acid in excess water, which of the following effects would be observed in the solution?

A. Decreased pH
B. Increased pH
C. Decreased pK_a
D. Increased pK_a

7. A certain chemical reaction follows the following rate law:

Rate = k $[NO_2]$ $[Br_2]$

Which of the following statements describe the kinetics of this reaction?

I. The reaction is a second-order reaction.
II. The amount of NO_2 consumed is equal to the amount of Br_2 consumed.
III. The rate will not be affected by the addition of a compound other than NO_2 and Br_2.

A. I only
B. I and II only
C. I and III only
D. III only

8. The following data shown in the table was collected for the combustion of the theoretical compound XH_4:

$$XH_4 + 2O_2 \rightarrow XO_2 + 2H_2O$$

Trial	$[XH_4]_{initial}$ (M)	$[O_2]_{initial}$ (M)	Rate (M/min)
1	0.6	0.6	12.4
2	0.6	2.4	49.9
3	1.2	2.4	198.3

What is the rate law for the reaction described here?

A. Rate = k $[XH_4]$ $[O_2]$
B. Rate = k $[XH_4]$ $[O_2]^2$
C. Rate = k $[XH_4]^2$ $[O_2]$
D. Rate = k $[XH_4]^2$ $[O_2]^2$

9. Which of the following actions does NOT affect the equilibrium of a reaction?

A. Adding/subtracting heat
B. Adding/removing a catalyst
C. Increasing/decreasing concentration of reactants
D. Increasing/decreasing volume of reactants

10. In a sealed 1 L container, 1 mol of nitrogen gas reacts with 3 mol of hydrogen gas to form 0.05 mol of NH_3. Which of the following is closest to the K_{eq} of the reaction?

A. 0.0001
B. 0.001
C. 0.01
D. 0.1

FOR QUESTIONS 11–13, CONSIDER THE FOLLOWING ENERGY DIAGRAM SHOWN IN FIGURE 1:

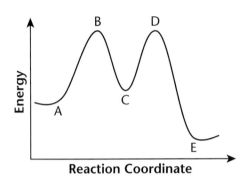

11. The overall reaction depicted by this energy diagram is

    A. endothermic, because point B is higher than point A.

    B. endothermic, because point C is higher than point A.

    C. exothermic, because point D is higher than point E.

    D. exothermic, because point A is higher than point E.

12. Which process has the highest activation energy?

    A. The first step of the forward reaction

    B. The first step of the reverse reaction

    C. The second step of the forward reaction

    D. The second step of the reverse reaction

13. Which of the following components of the reaction mechanism will NEVER be present in the reaction vessel when the reaction coordinate is at point B?

    A. Reactants

    B. Products

    C. Intermediates

    D. Catalysts

14. Consider the following two reactions:

$$3A + 2B \rightleftharpoons 3C + 4D \quad \text{(Reaction 1)}$$

$$4D + 3C \rightleftharpoons 3A + 2B \quad \text{(Reaction 2)}$$

If K_{eq} for reaction 1 is equal to 0.1, what is K_{eq} for reaction 2?

    A. 0.1

    B. 1

    C. 10

    D. 100

15. Which of the following statements would best describe the experimental result if the temperature of the following theoretical reaction were decreased?

$$A + B \rightleftharpoons C + D \quad \Delta H = -1.12 \text{ kJ/mol}$$

    A. [C] + [D] would increase

    B. [A] + [B] would increase

    C. ΔH would increase

    D. ΔH would decrease

16. Compound A has a K_a of approximately 10^{-4}. Which of the following compounds is most likely to react with a solution of compound A?

    A. HNO_2

    B. NO_2

    C. NH_3

    D. N_2O_5

17. The following system obeys second-order kinetics.

$$2NO_2 \rightarrow NO_3 + NO \qquad \text{(slow)}$$

$$NO_3 + CO \rightarrow NO_2 + CO_2 \qquad \text{(fast)}$$

What is the rate law for this reaction?

    A. Rate $= k\,[NO_2]\,[CO]$

    B. Rate $= k\,[NO_2]^2\,[CO]$

    C. Rate $= k\,[NO_2]\,[NO_3]$

    D. Rate $= k\,[NO_2]^2$

18. The potential energy diagram shown represents four different reactions.

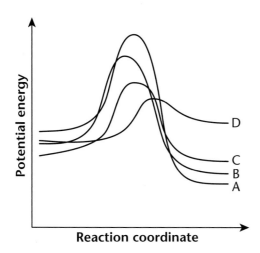

Assuming identical conditions, which of the reactions displayed on the energy diagram proceeds the fastest?

A. A
B. B
C. C
D. D

Small Group Questions

1. Because catalysts affect reaction rate, why don't we include their concentrations in reaction rate laws?

2. Do zero-order reactions contradict the Collision Theory of Chemical Kinetics?

3. How can Le Châtelier's principle be used to manipulate reactions?

Explanations to Practice Questions

1. D

Based on the information given in the question, the rate is first order with respect to the concentration of the first reactant; when the concentration of that reactant doubles, the rate also doubles. Because the reaction is third-order, the sum of the exponents in the rate law must be equal to 3. Therefore, the rate law is defined as follows:

$$\text{Rate} = k \, [\text{reactant 1}]^1 \, [\text{reactant 2}]^2$$

So, the concentration of reactant 2 must be squared in order to write a rate law that represents a third-order reaction. When the concentration of reactant 2 is multiplied by ½, the rate will be multiplied by $(½)^2 = ¼$.

2. A

Before you try to answer this question, you should draw a potential energy diagram for the system.

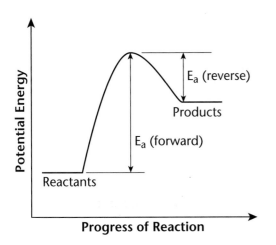

If the activation energy of the forward reaction is greater than the activation energy of the reverse reaction, then the products must have a higher enthalpy than the reactants. The overall energy of the system is higher at the end than it was in the beginning. The net enthalpy change is positive, indicating an endothermic reaction. Spontaneity is correlated with Gibbs free energy (ΔG).

3. A

Carbon dioxide gas evolves and leaves the bottle, which decreases the total pressure of the reactants. Le Châtelier's principle explains that a decrease in pressure shifts the equilibrium so as to increase the number of moles of gas present; this particular reaction will shift to the left, thereby decreasing the amount of carbonic acid and increasing the amount of carbon dioxide and water. Oxygen and nitrogen are not highly reactive and are unlikely to spontaneously combine with CO_2 or H_2CO_3.

4. D

ΔH is always positive for an endothermic reaction (meaning that option I is correct) and ΔG is always negative for a spontaneous reaction (meaning that option II is correct). Based on these two facts, ΔS can be determined by the free energy equation: $\Delta G = \Delta H - T\Delta S$, which can be rewritten as: $T\Delta S = \Delta H - \Delta G$. If ΔH is positive and ΔG is negative, $\Delta H - \Delta G$ must be positive. This means that $T\Delta S$ is positive. T (the temperature of the system in Kelvin) is always positive, so ΔS must also be positive. Therefore, option III is also correct. (A), (B), and (C) all include true but incomplete statements.

5. C

Recall that the K_{sp} of a salt is equal to the product of the concentrations of each of the salt's ions in saturated solution. Each molecule of this salt dissociates into three A^+ ions and one B^{3-} ion, so K_{sp} is equal to $[A^+][A^+][A^+][B^{3-}] = [A^+]^3[B^{3-}]$. The molar solubility of the salt is equal to the total number of moles of the salt in solution. The molar solubility of the salt is 10 M, thus the A^+ ion is present

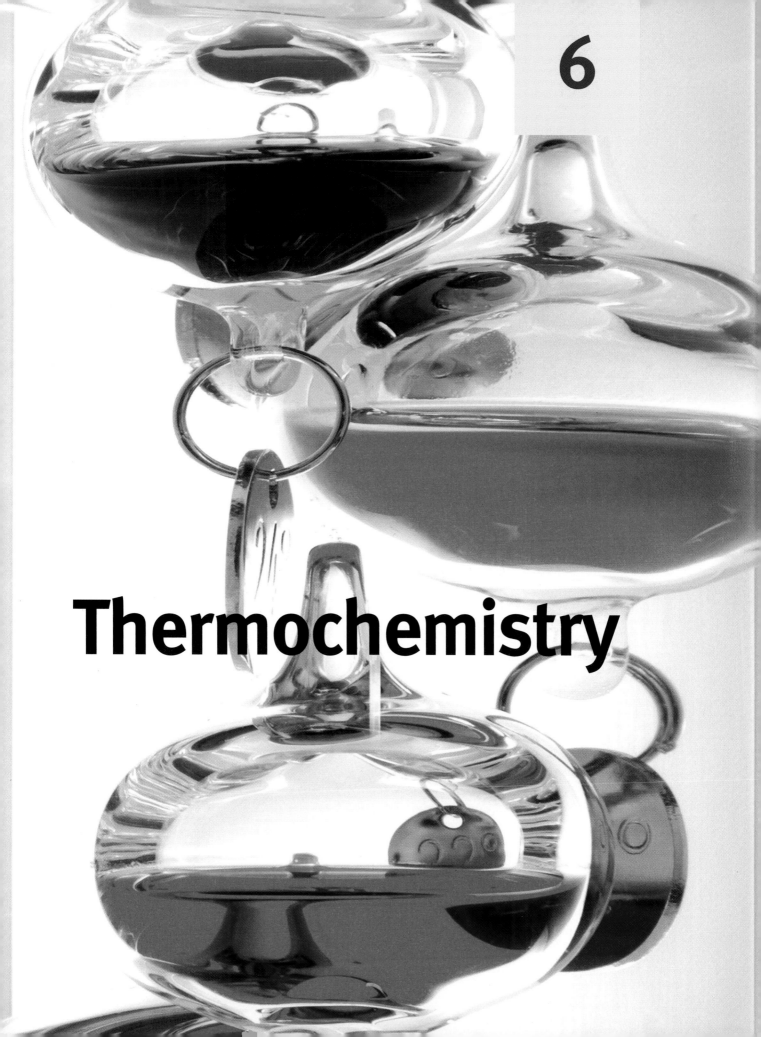

6

Thermochemistry

Back in the "bad old days" before people became aware of the environmental havoc wreaked by Styrofoam, we used to drink our coffee from Styrofoam cups. Now, of course, coffee is usually served in paper cups consisting of some percentage of post-consumer recycled material, enveloped in a thin cardboard sleeve (also typically made from recycled material) for added insulation against the hot contents. In those rare instances when coffee is served in Styrofoam, the bearer of the cup may receive a few withering glances from those especially passionate about environmentalism and at the very least will probably feel a little guilty for using it.

While Styrofoam might be bad for the environment, it is certainly a good insulator. That's why it was the material of choice for disposable coffee cups for so long: it keeps hot things (like coffee) hot, and cool things (like your hands—relative to the coffee) cool. The layer of Styrofoam protects your hands from too quickly absorbing the energy from the hot coffee and getting burned. Paper coffee cups just aren't as effective at insulation as Styrofoam cups are; hence the need for the cardboard sleeve as an extra layer of protection.

Styrofoam cups are such good insulators that they can be used as holding containers for certain calorimetry experiments. "Coffee-cup calorimetry," which uses Styrofoam cups to measure heats of solution and specific heats of metals and other materials, is low tech, yet can produce remarkably accurate results, as long as care has been taken to calibrate the calorimeter and to minimize heat loss through the top. The next time you are at your favorite overpriced coffee chain, standing at the milk and sugar station, think about what you are doing when you mix the cold milk into the hot coffee. What you have there in your hand is really a little science experiment. If you took the time to measure the masses and temperatures of the hot coffee and the cold milk before mixing them, measured the drink's temperature after you had stirred them up, and then looked up the specific heats for water and milk, you would have enough information to calculate the amount of heat exchanged between the hot coffee and the cold milk. (And if you *really* wanted to be accurate you would include in your calculation the mass of the little wooden stirrer and its specific heat as well!) Of course, if you actually used the milk and coffee station as your lab bench, you may be putting your life at risk in the hands of the angry, under- and overcaffeinated mob standing behind you impatiently waiting their turn.

This chapter will review the basic principles of thermochemistry, which is the study of the energy changes that accompany chemical and physical processes. Starting from the first law of thermodynamics, which states that energy is never created nor destroyed, but at most simply changed from one form to another, we will analyze the calculations that are done to quantify the various changes or exchanges in energy as a system moves from some initial state to a final state. As we go along, we will define what is meant by system and surroundings, state functions, heat, enthalpy, entropy, and Gibbs free energy.

Systems and Processes

For whatever reasons, students seem to have some anxiety over what, exactly, constitutes a system, and what, by exclusion from the system, constitute the surroundings or environment. Perhaps the problem isn't so much with the definitions, which are fairly straightforward, but the way in which the boundary between the two can be "moved" to suit the interests of the experimenter or observer. Simply put, the system is the matter that is being observed. It's the total amount of reactants and products, say, in a chemical reaction. It's the amount of solute and solvent used to create a solution. It could even be the gas inside a balloon. Then the surroundings or environment is everything outside of what you're looking at. However, the boundary between system and surroundings is not permanently fixed, and it can be moved. For example, you might consider the mass of coffee in your coffee cup to be the system and the cup containing it to be the environment. If this is the way you set your boundary, then you're probably interested in determining, say, the amount of heat transferred from the hot coffee to the cooler coffee cup. Alternatively, you might define the system as the hot coffee and the cup, and the environment as the air surrounding the coffee cup. If this is the way you've defined your boundary, then you're probably interested in the heat exchange between the hot coffee/cup system and the cooler surrounding air. The boundary can be extended out farther and farther, until ultimately the entire mass of the universe is included in the system, at which point there is no surroundings. Where you place the boundary is really a decision based on what matter you're interested in studying.

Systems can be further characterized by whether or not they can exchange heat and/ or matter with the surroundings. A system may be:

- **Isolated**—the system cannot exchange energy (heat and work) or matter with the surroundings; for example, an insulated bomb calorimeter.
- **Closed**—the system can exchange energy (heat and work), but not matter with the surroundings; for example, a steam radiator.
- **Open**—the system can exchange both energy (again, heat and work) and matter with the surroundings; for example, a pot of boiling water.

When a system experiences a change in one or more of its properties (such as concentration of reactant or product, temperature, or pressure) we say that it undergoes a **process.** While processes, by definition, are associated with changes of state of systems, some processes are uniquely identified by some property that is constant throughout the process. For example, **isothermal** processes occur when the system's temperature is constant. Constant temperature implies that the total internal energy of the system is constant throughout the process. **Adiabatic** processes occur when no heat is exchanged between the system and the environment, thus the heat content of the system is constant throughout the process. Finally, **isobaric** processes occur when the pressure of the system is constant. Isothermal and isobaric processes are common, because it is usually easy to control temperature and pressure.

Processes themselves can be also classified as spontaneous or nonspontaneous. A spontaneous process is one that can occur by itself without having to be driven by energy from an outside source. Calculating the change in the Gibbs free energy (ΔG) for a process, such as a chemical reaction, allows us to predict whether the process will be spontaneous or nonspontaneous. The same quantities that are used to calculate the change in the Gibbs free energy, ΔH and ΔS, can also tell us whether or not the process will be temperature-dependent, that is, spontaneous at some temperatures and nonspontaneous at others (see the section on Gibbs free energy).

Spontaneous reactions, as you'll recall from our discussion of chemical kinetics and equilibrium in Chapter 5, will not necessarily happen quickly and may not go to completion. Many spontaneous reactions have very high activation energies and therefore rarely actually take place. For example, when was the last time you saw a match ignite itself spontaneously? Or for that matter, when was the last time you or a loved one spontaneously combusted? However, provide an amount of thermal energy (generated by the friction associated with "striking the match") that equals or exceeds the energy of activation, and the match will light and burn spontaneously. Combustion, the combination of the chemical components of the match with molecular oxygen in the air, will not need any additional external energy input in order to proceed once the energy of activation has been supplied. Some spontaneous reactions proceed very slowly. The role of enzymes, biological catalysts, is to selectively enhance the rate of certain spontaneous but slow chemical reactions so that the biologically necessary products can be formed at a rate sufficient for sustaining life. As we learned in Chapter 5, some reactions do not go to completion but settle into a low-energy state called equilibrium. Spontaneous reactions may go to completion, but many simply reach equilibrium with dynamically stable concentrations of reactants and products.

States and State Functions

Every year in January, the President of the United States speaks to the nation in a State of the Union address. In the speech, the President gives an assessment of the parameters by which we can measure the relative well-being of the nation and its citizens. There is usually discussion of war or peace, economic indicators, domestic programs, and other measurements of the social, political, and economic status of the country. These indicators help the people understand where they "are" as a nation in comparison to where they were the year prior, but less so how they got to where they are now.

Similarly, the state of a system is described by certain macroscopic properties of the system. These properties, or state functions, describe the system in an equilibrium state. They cannot describe the process of the system, that is, how the system got to its current equilibrium; they are useful only for comparing one equilibrium state to another. The pathway taken from one equilibrium state to another is described quantitatively by the process functions, the most important of which are mechanical work (W) and heat (Q).

The state functions include temperature (T), pressure (P), volume (V), density (ρ), internal energy (E or U), enthalpy (H), entropy (S), and Gibbs free energy (G). When the state of a system changes from one equilibrium to another, one or more of these state functions will change. In addition, while state functions are independent of the path (process) taken, they are not necessarily independent of one another. For example, Gibbs free energy is related to enthalpy, entropy, and temperature, as you will see.

MCAT Expertise

On the MCAT, be sure that you do not confuse standard conditions in thermodynamics with standard temperature and pressure (STP) in gas law calculations. (See Chapter 7.)

Because systems can be in different equilibrium states at different temperatures and pressures, a set of **standard conditions** has been defined for measuring the enthalpy, entropy, and Gibbs free energy changes of a reaction. The standard conditions are defined as 25°C (298 K) and 1 atm. Don't confuse standard conditions with **standard temperature and pressure (STP)** for which the temperature is 0°C (273 K) and 1 atm. This is a common MCAT Test Day mistake and one that is easily made but can be easily avoided. You'll use standard conditions for thermodynamic problems of enthalpy or free energy, but you'll use STP for ideal gas calculations.

Under standard conditions, the most stable form of a substance is called the **standard state** of that substance. You should recognize the standard states for some elements and compounds commonly encountered on the test. For example, H_2 (g), H_2O (l), NaCl (s), O_2 (g), and C (s) (graphite) are the most stable forms of these substances under standard conditions. Recognizing whether or not a substance is in its standard state is important for thermochemical calculations such as heats of reactions and in particular, the heat of formation. The changes in enthalpy, entropy, and free energy that occur when a reaction takes place under standard conditions are called the **standard enthalpy**, **standard entropy**, and **standard free energy** changes, respectively, and are symbolized by $\Delta H°$, $\Delta S°$, and $\Delta G°$.

The rest of this chapter will focus on the following state functions: enthalpy, entropy (energy dispersal), and free energy, with some concluding remarks on spontaneity.

Heat

Before we can examine the first of the four state functions that are the focus of this chapter, we must address the topic of heat, which is a source of some confusion for students. Perhaps the greatest barrier to a proper understanding of heat is the semantic conflation of the terms *heat* and *temperature*. Many people use these terms interchangeably in everyday conversation. We might say, for example, that a midsummer afternoon was unbearably hot or that the temperature exceeded 100°F. Both convey the sense that the day was very, very warm, but what makes sense in everyday conversation needs to be clarified for a proper understanding of thermochemical principles. **Temperature (*T*)** is related to the average kinetic energy of the particles of the substance whose temperature is being measured. Temperature is the way that we scale how hot or cold something is (but not necessarily how hot or cold something feels to us: for reasons that will become clear in our discussion of specific heat, blacktop will feel hotter to our bare feet than a wooden boardwalk would even if they are at the same temperature). We are familiar with a few temperature scales: Fahrenheit, Celsius, and Kelvin. The average kinetic energy of the particles in a substance is related to the thermal energy of the substance, but because we must also include consideration of how much substance is present to calculate total thermal energy content, the most we can say about temperature is that when a substance's thermal energy increases, its temperature increases also. Nevertheless, we cannot say that something that is hot necessarily has greater thermal energy (in absolute terms) than a substance that is cold. For example, we might determine that a large amount of cool water has greater *total* heat content than a very small amount of very hot water.

Heat (*Q*) is the transfer of energy from one substance to another as a result of their difference in temperature. In fact, the zeroth law of thermodynamics implies that objects are in thermal equilibrium only when their temperatures are equal. Heat is therefore a process function, not a state function: we can quantify how much thermal energy is transferred between two or more objects as a result of their difference in temperatures by measuring the heat transferred.

The first law of thermodynamics states that the change in the total internal energy (ΔU) of a system is equal to the amount of heat (thermal energy) transferred (Q) to the system minus the amount of work (W) (another form of energy transfer by the application of force through displacement) done by the system. This can be expressed mathematically as:

$$\Delta U = Q - W$$

> ## Key Concept
> Remember that heat and temperature are different; heat is a specific form of energy that can enter or leave a system, while temperature is a measure of the average kinetic energy of the particles in a system.

Because heat and work are measured independently, we can assess the transfer of energy in the form of heat through any process regardless of the work done (or not done). Processes in which the system absorbs heat are called endothermic ($+\Delta Q$), while those processes in which the system releases heat are called exothermic ($-\Delta Q$). The unit of heat is the unit of energy: Joule (J) or calorie (c) for which 1 c = 4.184 J.

You know how people who live in really hot desert climates, when asked, "How can you stand the heat?" often respond by pointing out, "But it's a dry heat!"? Well, there's some truth to that. One of the most important ways that the body works to prevent overheating is through the production of sweat—that exocrine secretion of water, electrolytes, and urea. However, it's not the production of sweat, per se, that is the cooling mechanism. It's the evaporation of the sweat that helps cool the body. Evaporation (vaporization) from the liquid to gas phase is an endothermic process: energy must be absorbed in order for the particles of the liquid to gain enough kinetic energy to escape into the gas phase. So the sweat that is excreted onto the skin must absorb energy in order to evaporate. Where does that necessary energy come from? It comes from the body itself. Hot, arid desert air has lower partial pressure of water vapor than humid tropical air, so sweat vaporizes more readily in the dry air than it does in the humid air. Although it might be hard to believe that any temperature in excess of 100°F could ever be considered comfortable, it probably is true that most people will feel more comfortable in "dry heat" than in "tropical heat."

When substances of different temperatures are brought into thermal contact with each other (that is, some physical arrangement that allows for the transfer of heat energy), energy—in the form of heat—will transfer from the warmer substance to the cooler substance. When a substance undergoes a chemical reaction that is exothermic or endothermic, heat energy will be exchanged between the system and the environment. The process of measuring transferred heat is called calorimetry. Two basic types of calorimetry that you should know and understand for Test Day include constant-pressure calorimetry and constant-volume calorimetry. The coffee-cup calorimeter, introduced at the beginning of this lesson, is a low-tech example of a constant-pressure calorimeter, while the bomb calorimeter is an example of a constant-volume calorimeter. "Constant-pressure" and "constant-volume" are terms used to describe the conditions under which the heat changes are measured.

The heat (q) absorbed or released in a given process is calculated from the equation:

$$q = mc\Delta T$$

where m is the mass, c is the **specific heat** of the substance, and ΔT is the change in temperature (in either Celsius or Kelvin). Specific heat is the amount of energy required to raise the temperature of one gram or kilogram of a substance by one

Key Concept

Endothermic: positive ΔH

Exothermic: negative ΔH

degree Celsius or one unit Kelvin. Specific heat values will be provided for you on Test Day, but one value that you need to remember is the specific heat of H_2O (l): one calorie per gram per Celsius degree (1 c/g°C). Speaking of easy to remember, you ought not have any problem remembering this equation, given that $q = mc\Delta T$ looks like "q equals MCAT".

Constant-Volume Calorimetry

To picture the setup of a constant-pressure calorimeter, just think of the coffee-cup calorimeter: an insulated container covered with a lid and filled with a solution in which a reaction or some physical process, such as dissolution, is occurring. The pressure, which is just the atmospheric pressure, remains constant throughout the process. The setup of a constant-volume calorimeter is perhaps a little less familiar to you or harder to picture. Furthermore, the term *bomb calorimeter* sounds rather ominous. Well, don't worry—this isn't some relic from the Cold War. Perhaps "bomb" is a bit misleading: a more accurately descriptive term is "decomposition vessel." This is better reflective of what is actually taking place. A sample of matter, typically a hydrocarbon, is placed in the steel decomposition vessel, which is then filled with almost pure O_2 gas. The decomposition vessel is then placed in an insulated container holding a known mass of water. The contents of the decomposition vessel are ignited by an electric ignition mechanism. The material combusts (burns) in the presence of the oxygen and the heat that is evolved in the combustion is the heat of the reaction. Because $W = P\Delta V$, no work is done in an isovolumic ($\Delta V = 0$) process, so $W_{calorimeter} = 0$. Furthermore, because of the insulation, the whole calorimeter can be considered isolated from the rest of the universe and so we can identify the "system" as the sample plus oxygen and steel, and the surroundings as the water. Because no heat is exchanged between the calorimeter and the rest of the universe, $Q_{calorimeter}$ is 0. So, $\Delta U_{system} + \Delta U_{surroundings} = \Delta U_{calorimeter} = Q_{calorimeter} - W_{calorimeter} = 0$. Therefore, $\Delta U_{system} = -\Delta U_{surroundings}$. Because no work is done, $q_{system} = -q_{surroundings}$: and $m_{steel}c_{steel}\Delta T + m_{oxygen}c_{oxygen}\Delta T = -m_{water}c_{water}\Delta T$.

Note that by using the layer of insulation to isolate the entire calorimeter from the rest of the universe, we've created an adiabatic process. This means that no heat is exchanged between the calorimeter and the rest of the universe, but it *is* exchanged between the steel decomposition vessel and the surrounding water. As the previous derivation shows, heat exchange between the system and its surroundings makes it possible for us to calculate the heat of the combustion.

Enthalpy ★★★★☆

Most reactions in the lab occur under constant pressure (at 1 atm) in closed thermodynamic systems. To express heat changes at constant pressure, chemists use the term **enthalpy (*H*).** Enthalpy is a state function, so we can calculate the change in enthalpy (ΔH) for a system that has undergone a process, for example, a chemical reaction, by comparing the enthalpy of the final state to the enthalpy of the initial state, irrespective of the path taken. The change in enthalpy is equal to the heat transferred into or out of the system at constant pressure. To find the enthalpy change of a reaction, ΔH_{rxn}, you must subtract the enthalpy of the reactants from the enthalpy of the products:

$$\Delta H_{rxn} = H_{products} - H_{reactants}$$

A positive ΔH_{rxn} corresponds to an endothermic process, and a negative ΔH_{rxn} corresponds to an exothermic process. It is not possible to measure enthalpy directly; only ΔH can be measured, and even then, only for certain fast and spontaneous processes. Several standard methods have been developed to calculate ΔH for any process.

Standard Heat of Formation

The **standard enthalpy of formation** of a compound, ΔH°_f, is the enthalpy change that would occur if one mole of a compound in its standard state was formed directly from its elements in their respective standard states. Remember that standard state is the most stable physical state of an element or compound at 298 K and 1 atm. Note that ΔH°_f of an element in its standard state, by definition, is zero. The ΔH°_f's of most known substances are tabulated. You do not need to memorize these values as they will be provided for you as necessary.

Standard Heat of Reaction

The **standard heat of a reaction**, ΔH°_{rxn}, is the hypothetical enthalpy change that would occur if the reaction were carried out under standard conditions. What this means is that all reactants must be in their standard states and all products must be in their standard states. This can be calculated by taking the difference between the sum of the standard heats of formation for the products and the sum of the standard heats of formation of the reactants:

$$\Delta H^\circ_{rxn} = \sum(\Delta H^\circ_f \text{ of products}) - \sum(\Delta H^\circ_f \text{ of reactants})$$

Hess's Law

Enthalpy is a state function and is a property of the equilibrium state, so the pathway taken for a process is irrelevant to the change in enthalpy from one equilibrium state to another. As a consequence of this, **Hess's law** states that enthalpy changes of reactions are additive. When thermochemical equations (chemical equations for which energy changes are known) are added to give the net equation for a reaction, the corresponding heats of reaction are also added to give the net heat of reaction. You can think of Hess's law as being embodied in the enthalpy

Key Concept

State functions are path-independent. Always.

absorbed by the system in order to overcome the bonding force. Since energy is absorbed, the bond breaking reaction is endothermic.

If you have a hard time remembering whether bond formation or dissociation is endothermic, think about bonds as if they were two bar magnets stuck together. You have to exert pulling forces (invest energy) in order to pull apart two bar magnets (endothermic). On the other hand, the two bar magnets, once separated, "want" to come back together because they exert an attractive force between their opposite poles. Allowing them to stick together reduces their potential energy (exothermic).

Example: Calculate the enthalpy change for the following reaction:

$$C(s) + 2 H_2(g) \rightarrow CH_4(g) \quad \Delta H = ?$$

Bond dissociation energies of H–H and C–H bonds are 436 kJ/mol and 415 kJ/mol, respectively.

$$\Delta H_f \text{ of } C(g) = 715 \text{ kJ/mol}$$

Solution: CH_4 is formed from free elements in their standard states (C in solid and H_2 in gaseous state).

Thus here, $\Delta H_{rxn} = \Delta H_f$

The reaction can be written in three steps:
    a) $C(s) \rightarrow C(g)$ ΔH_1
    b) $2 [H_2(g) \rightarrow 2 H(g)]$ $2\Delta H_2$
    c) $C(g) + 4 H(g) \rightarrow CH_4(g)$ ΔH_3

and $\Delta H_f = [\Delta H_1 + 2\Delta H_2] + [\Delta H_3]$

$$\Delta H_1 = \Delta H_f C(g) = 715 \text{ kJ/mol,}$$

ΔH_2 is the energy required to break the H–H bond of one mole of H_2. So:

$$\Delta H_2 = \text{bond energy of } H_2$$
$$= 436 \text{ kJ/mol}$$

ΔH_3 is the energy released when 4 C–H bonds are formed. So:

$$\Delta H_3 = -(4 \times \text{bond energy of C–H})$$
$$= -(4 \times 415 \text{ kJ/mol})$$
$$= -1,660 \text{ kJ/mol}$$

(**Note:** Because energy is released when bonds are formed, ΔH_3 is negative.)

Therefore:

$$\Delta H_{rxn} = \Delta H_f = [715 + 2(436)] - (1,660) \text{ kJ/mol}$$
$$= -73 \text{ kJ/mol}$$

MCAT Expertise

With practice, you'll become accustomed to patterns and shortcuts that will make things easier on Test Day.

Key Concept

The larger the alkane reactant, the more numerous the combustion products.

Key Concept

Entropy changes that accompany phase changes (see Chapter 8) can be easily estimated, at least qualitatively. For example, freezing is accompanied by a decrease in entropy as the relatively disordered liquid becomes a well-ordered solid. Meanwhile, boiling is accompanied by a large increase in entropy as the liquid becomes a much more highly disordered gas. For any substance, sublimation will be the phase transition with the greatest entropy change.

Heats of Combustion

One more type of standard enthalpy change that you should be aware of for the MCAT is the **standard heat of combustion**, ΔH°_{comb}. Because measurements of enthalpy change require a reaction to be spontaneous and fast, combustion reactions are the ideal process for such measurements. Most combustion reactions presented on the MCAT occur in the presence of O_2 in the atmosphere, but keep in mind that there are other combustion reactions in which oxygen is not the oxidant. Diatomic fluorine, for example, can be used as an oxidant and hydrogen gas will combust with chlorine gas to form gaseous hydrochloric acid and, in the process, will evolve a large amount of heat and light characteristic of combustion reactions. The reactions listed in the C_3H_8 (g) example shown earlier are combustion reactions with O_2 (g) as the oxidant. Therefore, the enthalpy change listed for each of the three reactions is the ΔH_{comb} for each of the reactions.

Entropy

Many, many students are genuinely perplexed by the concept of entropy. Enthalpy makes, perhaps, intuitive sense, especially when the energy change from reactants to products is large, fast, and dramatic (as in combustion reactions involving explosions). Entropy seems to be less intuitive. Except that it isn't. In fact, our understanding of what constitutes normal life experience and even the passage of time is based, fundamentally, upon the property of entropy. Consider, for example, how "normal" each of the following seems to you: hot tea cools down, frozen drinks melt, iron rusts, buildings crumble, balloons deflate, living things die, and so on.

These examples have a common denominator; in all of them, energy of some form or another is going from being localized or concentrated to being spread out or dispersed. The thermal energy in the hot tea is spreading out to the cooler air that surrounds it. The thermal energy in the warmer air is spreading out to the cooler frozen drink. The chemical energy in the bonds of elemental iron and oxygen is released and dispersed as a result of the formation of the more stable (lower energy) bonds of iron oxide (rust). The potential energy of the building is released and dispersed in the form of light, sound, and heat (motional energy) of the ground and air as the building crumbles and falls. The motional energy of the pressurized air is released to the surrounding atmosphere as the balloon deflates. The chemical energy of all the molecules and atoms in living flesh is released into the environment during the process of death and decay.

This is the **second law of thermodynamics**: energy spontaneously disperses from being localized to becoming spread out if it is not hindered from doing so. Pay attention to this: *the usual way of thinking about entropy as disorder must not be taken too literally, a trap that many students fall into. Be very careful in thinking* system. We explored the various ways Hess's law can be applied to calculate the total enthalpy change for a series of reactions. Moving on to entropy, we described this property as a measure of the degree to which energy in a system becomes spread out through a process. There is danger in thinking too literally about entropy as "disorder," as a system's entropy may be increasing even if there is no observable change in the system's macroscopic disorder (e.g., ice warming from $-10°C$ to $-5°C$). Gibbs free energy combines enthalpy and entropy considerations, and the change in Gibbs function determines whether a process will be spontaneous or nonspontaneous. When the change in Gibbs function is negative, the process is spontaneous, but when the change in Gibbs function is positive, the process is nonspontaneous.

Great job! This is a difficult material, but your focus and attention to these topics will pay off in points on Test Day. The changes in energy that accompany chemical processes are tested heavily on the MCAT.

CONCEPTS TO REMEMBER

☐ Systems can be characterized as isolated (no heat or matter exchange), closed (no matter exchange), or open (both heat and matter exchange possible).

☐ Some processes are identified by some constant property of the system: isothermal (constant internal energy/temperature), adiabatic (no heat exchange), and isobaric (constant pressure).

☐ State functions are physical properties of a system that describe the equilibrium state; as such, changes in state functions are pathway-independent. Some examples of state functions are temperature, volume, pressure, internal energy, enthalpy, entropy, and Gibbs free energy.

☐ Standard state of a substance is the most stable form (phase) of the substance under standard state conditions (298 K and 1 atm). Standard enthalpy, standard entropy, and standard free energy changes are measured under standard state conditions.

☐ Heat and temperature are not the same thing. Temperature is a scale related to the average kinetic energy of the molecules in a substance. Heat is the transfer of energy that results from two objects at different temperatures being put in thermal contact with each other. Heat energy transferred from one substance to another is measured by the methods of calorimetry.

☐ Enthalpy is a measure of the potential energy of a system found in the intermolecular interactions and bonds of molecules. Hess's law states that the total change in the potential energy of a system is equal to the changes in potential energies of the individual steps (reactions) of the process.

☐ Entropy is a measure of the degree to which energy has been spread out through a system or between a system and its surroundings. It is a ratio of heat transferred per unit Kelvin. Systems reach maximum possible entropy (maximum possible energy dispersal) only at equilibrium.

☐ Gibbs free energy is a calculation involving both enthalpy and entropy values for a system. The change in Gibbs function determines whether a process is spontaneous or nonspontaneous. When the change in Gibbs function is negative, the process is spontaneous, but when the change in Gibbs function is positive, the process is nonspontaneous.

☐ Temperature-dependent processes are those that change between spontaneous and nonspontaneous at a certain temperature. For example; water freezes spontaneously only at temperatures below 273 K, and boils spontaneously only at temperatures above 373 K.

☐ The larger and more positive the value of the equilibrium constant is, the more spontaneous a reaction will be (that is, the more negative the change in Gibbs function for the system as it moves from its initial position to its equilibrium).

EQUATIONS TO REMEMBER

☐ $U = Q - W$

☐ $q = mc\Delta T$

☐ $\Delta H^{\circ}_{rxn} = \sum(\Delta H^{\circ}_{f} \text{ of products}) - \sum(\Delta H^{\circ}_{f} \text{ of reactants})$

☐ $\Delta H_{rxn} = \sum\Delta H_{\text{bonds broken}} + \sum\Delta H_{\text{bonds formed}}$

☐ $\Delta S = \dfrac{Q_{rev}}{T}$

☐ $\Delta S^{\circ}_{rxn} = \sum\Delta S^{\circ}_{\text{products}} - \sum\Delta S^{\circ}_{\text{reactants}}$

☐ $\Delta G^{\circ}_{rxn} = \sum(\Delta G^{\circ}_{f} \text{ of products}) - \sum(\Delta G^{\circ}_{f} \text{ of reactants})$

☐ $\Delta G^{\circ}_{rxn} = -RT \ln K_{eq}$

☐ $\Delta G_{rxn} = RT \ln\left(\dfrac{Q}{K_{eq}}\right)$

Practice Questions

1. Consider the cooling of an ideal gas in a closed system. This process is illustrated in the pressure-volume graph shown in Figure 1.

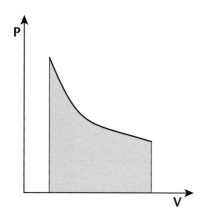

Based on the information in Figure 1, the process is

A. adiabatic.
B. isobaric.
C. isothermal.
D. Two of the above

2. A reaction has a positive entropy and enthalpy. What can be inferred about the progress of this reaction from this information?

A. The reaction is spontaneous.
B. The reaction is nonspontaneous.
C. The reaction is at equilibrium.
D. There is not enough information to determine if the reaction is spontaneous.

3. Pure sodium metal spontaneously combusts upon contact with room temperature water. What is true about the equilibrium constant of this combustion reaction at 25°C?

A. $K_{eq} < 1$
B. $K_{eq} > 1$
C. $K_{eq} = 1$
D. There is not enough information to determine the equilibrium constant.

4. Which of the following processes has the most exothermic heat of reaction?

A. Combustion of ethane
B. Combustion of propane
C. Combustion of *n*-butane
D. Combustion of isobutane

5. Methanol reacts with acetic acid to form methyl acetate and water as shown in the following table in the presence of an acid catalyst.

$$CH_3OH \text{ (l)} + CH_3COOH \text{ (aq)} \longrightarrow CH_3COOCH_3 \text{ (aq)} + H_2O \text{ (l)}$$

Type of Bond	Bond Disassociation Energy (kJ/mol)
C — C	348
C — H	413
C ═ O	805
O — H	464
C — O	360

What is the heat of formation of methyl acetate in kJ/mol?

A. −464 kJ/mol
B. +464 kJ/mol
C. −1,288 kJ/mol
D. +1,288 kJ/mol

6. At standard temperature and pressure, a chemical process is at equilibrium. What is the free energy of reaction (ΔG) for this process?

A. $\Delta G > 0$
B. $\Delta G < 0$
C. $\Delta G = 0$
D. There is not enough information to determine the free energy of reaction.

7. For a certain chemical process, $\Delta G° = -4.955$ kJ/mol. What is the equilibrium constant K_{eq} for this reaction?

A. $K_{eq} = 0.13$
B. $K_{eq} = 7.4$
C. $K_{eq} = 8.9$
D. $K_{eq} = 100$

8. Consider the chemical reaction in the vessel depicted in the following diagram.

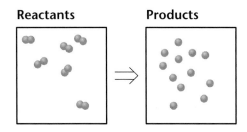

Reactants   **Products**

A. The reaction is spontaneous.
B. The reaction is nonspontaneous.
C. The reaction is at equilibrium.
D. There is not enough information to determine if the reaction is spontaneous.

9. Suppose $\Delta G_{rxn}° = -2,000$ kJ/mol for a chemical reaction. At 300 K, what is the reaction quotient Q?

A. $\Delta G = -2,000$ kJ/mol + (300 K) (8.314 Jmol^{-1}K^{-1})$ln(Q)$.
B. $\Delta G = -2,000$ kJ/mol − (300 K) (8.314 Jmol^{-1}K^{-1})$ln(Q)$.
C. $\Delta G = -2,000$ kJ/mol + (300 K) (8.314 Jmol^{-1}K^{-1})$log(Q)$.
D. $\Delta G = -2,000$ kJ/mol − (300 K) (8.314 Jmol^{-1}K^{-1})$log(Q)$.

10. An ideal gas undergoes a reversible expansion at constant pressure. Which of the following terms could describe this expansion?

I. Adiabatic
II. Isothermal
III. Isobaric

A. I only
B. I and II only
C. I and III only
D. I, II, and III

11. A chemical reaction has a negative enthalpy and a negative entropy. Which of the following terms describes the energy of this reaction?

   A. Exothermic

   B. Endothermic

   C. Endergonic

   D. Exergonic

12. Consider the chemical reaction in the vessel pictured in the following figure.

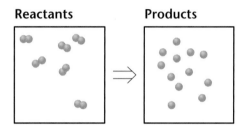

What can we say about the entropy of this reaction?

   A. $\Delta S > 0$

   B. $\Delta S < 0$

   C. $\Delta S = 0$

   D. There is not enough information in the picture to determine ΔS.

13. Which of the following statements is true of a spontaneous reaction?

   A. $\Delta G > 0$ and $K_{eq} > 1$

   B. $\Delta G > 0$ and $K_{eq} < 1$

   C. $\Delta G < 0$ and $K_{eq} > 1$

   D. $\Delta G < 0$ and $K_{eq} > 1$

14. Which of the following devices would be the most appropriate to use to measure the heat capacity of a liquid?

   A. Thermometer

   B. Calorimeter

   C. Barometer

   D. Volumetric flask

15. Which of the following equations does not state a law of thermodynamics?

   A. $\Delta E_{system} + \Delta E_{surroundings} = \Delta E_{universe}$

   B. $\Delta S_{system} + \Delta S_{surroundings} = \Delta S_{universe}$

   C. $\Delta H_{system} + \Delta H_{surroundings} = \Delta H_{universe}$

   D. $S_{universe} = 0$ at $T = 0$ K

16. A reaction coordinate for a chemical reaction is displayed in the graph below.

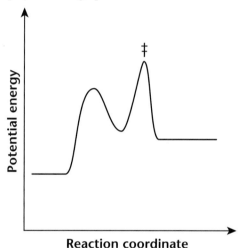

Which of the following terms describes the energy of this reaction?

   A. Endothermic

   B. Exothermic

   C. Endergonic

   D. Exergonic

Small Group Questions

1. Why is energy required to break bonds? Why is it released when bonds are formed?

2. Why is ΔH so much easier to determine than instantaneous H (enthalpy)? What standard methods have been developed to help scientists find H through calculations?

3. What is the difference between exergonic and exothermic? What is the difference between endergonic and endothermic?

Explanations to Practice Questions

1. A

The process is adiabatic. "Adiabatic" describes any thermodynamic transformation that does not involve a heat transfer (Q). An adiabatic process can be either reversible or irreversible, though for MCAT purposes, adiabatic expansions or contractions refer to volume changes in a closed system without experimentally significant losses or gains of heat. The internal energy of the system changes ($U = -P\Delta V$, where $U = Q - W$, $W = P\Delta V$, and $Q = 0$). (B) is incorrect because isobaric processes occur at constant pressures. (C) is incorrect because an isothermal process requires a heat transfer at constant temperature, and there is no heat transfer along an adiabatic curve. Once it becomes clear that the process is adiabatic, that rules out (D).

2. D

There is not enough information in the problem to determine whether or not the reaction is nonspontaneous. Start with $\Delta G = \Delta H - T\Delta S$. If the signs of enthalpy and entropy are the same, the reaction is temperature-dependent. If the signs of these terms are different, we can find the sign of ΔG without using temperature. The most common thermochemistry questions on the MCAT test your ability to manipulate and interpret the $\Delta G = \Delta H - T\Delta S$ equation. Memorize it.

3. B

Sodium oxidizes easily at standard conditions. No calculation is necessary here. There is enough information in the problem to predict the equilibrium constant, eliminating (D). If $K_{eq} < 1$, the reverse reaction is favored, indicating that the forward reaction is nonspontaneous. If $K_{eq} = 1$, the reaction is at equilibrium. If $K_{eq} > 1$, the forward reaction proceeds spontaneously. The question states that the sample spontaneously combusts at room temperature, i.e., 25°C. The answer is (B), $K_{eq} > 1$.

4. C

Combustion involves the reaction of a hydrocarbon with oxygen to produce carbon dioxide and water. Longer hydrocarbon chains yield greater amounts of combustion products and release more heat in the process (i.e., the reaction is more exothermic). Isobutane combusts less easily than *n*-butane because of its branched structure.

5. A

At first glance, this might seem like a math-heavy problem, but it really doesn't require any calculations at all. We just have to keep track of which bonds are broken and which bonds are formed. Remember, breaking bonds requires energy, while forming bonds releases energy.

Nucleophile: methanol's oxygen CH_3O-H
Electrophile: acetic acid's carbonyl carbon CH_3COOH

Through nucleophilic attack and leaving group separation, substitution occurs so that CH_3O takes the place of acetic acid's OH, to create methyl acetate. A proton transfer occurs between methanol and acetic acid's leaving group, OH.

Bonds broken:
1 O–H (–464 kJ/mol): proton leaves methanol
1 C–O (–360 kJ/mol): between the carbonyl carbon and the hydroxyl oxygen in acetic acid

Bonds formed:
1 C–O (+360 kJ/mol): between the carbonyl carbon and the attacking oxygen
1 O–H (+464 kJ/mol): between the leaving group oxygen and the transferred proton

The sum of all our bonding events is 0 kJ. We can reason through this intuitively. If one O–H bond is broken and another is made, the two values will cancel each other out and the net energy change must be 0 kJ. Similarly, if one C–O bond is broken and another is made, the net energy change will also be 0 kJ.

6. C

Standard temperature and pressure indicates 0°C and 1 atm. Gibbs free energy is temperature-dependent. If a reaction is at equilibrium, $\Delta G = 0$. (C) is the correct answer.

7. B

The correct answer is (B), using $K_{eq} = e^{-\Delta G°/RT}$ from $\Delta G° = -RT\ln(K_{eq})$. Use $e = 2.7$. R is the gas constant, 8.314 Jmol^{-1}K^{-1}, and $T = 298$ K, because of the standard-state sign.

Convert −4.955 kJ to −4,955 J, and then round −4,955 to −5,000. Let's also round 298 K to 300 K. The exponent's denominator will be 8.314 × 300, which we can estimate as 2,500.

$$\frac{-G°}{RT} = \frac{-(-4,955.14 \text{ J/mol})}{(8.314 \text{ J mol}^{-1}\text{K}^{-1})(298 \text{ K})} = \frac{5,000 \text{ J}}{2,500} = 2$$

So, we're left with $e^{(-5,000/-2,500)} = K_{eq}$, or $e^2 = K_{eq}$.

Plugging in 2.7 for e, we can calculate $2.7^{(2)} = K_{eq}$. Because 2^2 is 4 and 3^2 is 9, we can assume that we want an answer choice somewhere in between, which eliminates (A) and (D). Let's use some logic to choose between (B) and (C). Obviously, 8.9 is very close to 9, so we can assume that its square root is very, very close to 3 (it's actually around 2.984). The answer choice should be a bit smaller, so (B), 7.4, is correct.

8. D

There is not enough information available to determine the energy of this reaction. Only its entropy is obvious.

9. A

This problem asks you to calculate the free energy of reaction at non-standard conditions, which you can do using the equation $\Delta G = \Delta G° + RT\ln(Q)$. (R is the gas constant, 8.314 Jmol^{-1}K^{-1}).

10. C

There is not enough information to deduce anything about reaction temperature, which eliminates (B) and (D). Adiabatic and isothermal processes are necessarily opposite because adiabatic processes do not involve heat transfers. A reaction at constant pressure can be either adiabatic (no heat transfer to change volume) or isobaric (constant pressure, as the word roots imply).

11. A

This question requires interpreting the equation $\Delta G = \Delta H - T\Delta S$. Endergonic indicates a nonspontaneous reaction, and an exergonic reaction indicates a spontaneous reaction. In contrast, endothermic and exothermic reactions suggest the sign of the enthalpy of the reaction. The problem does not provide enough information to determine the free energy of this temperature-dependent reaction. (A) is the correct answer.

12. A

Disorder in the vessel increases over the course of the reaction, so (A) is correct. While we cannot make a quantitative determination of entropy from the picture, we can estimate the relative amount of disorder from the beginning to the end of the reaction in the vessel.

13. C

This is a definition question. A spontaneous reaction's free energy is negative by convention. Its equilibrium constant is greater than 1 because it is not at equilibrium and moves in the forward direction. (C) is the correct answer. (A), (B), and (D) are opposites.

14. B

A calorimeter measures specific heat or heat capacity. Though calorimeters often incorporate thermometers, the thermometer itself only tracks heat transfers, not the specific heat value itself, so (A) is incorrect. (C) is irrelevant; barometers measure changes in pressure. (D) is also incorrect as volumetric flasks measure liquid quantities, not the heat capacity of the liquid.

15. C

Memorize the laws of thermodynamics prior to Test Day; they may be stated in several different forms. You should know the equation and how to rephrase it into a sentence or two. The first law often confuses students—keep in mind that it refers to the overall energy of the universe, and not to the enthalpy of the universe, even though enthalpy is usually substituted for this term in introductory college chemistry experiments. The third law (absolute zero) is not an equation, so keep that in mind as you work.

16. A

Eliminate (C) and (D), which describe the free energy of reaction and cannot be determined from this graph. If the heat of formation of the products is greater than that of the reactants, the reaction is endothermic. We can determine this information by their relative magnitude on the graph. An exothermic graph would reflect products with a lower enthalpy than that of the reactants.

as such will be smaller for gases that are small and less polarizable (such as helium) and larger for gases that are larger and more polarizable (such as Xe or N_2) and largest for polar molecules such as HCl and NH_3. The b term corrects for the volume of the molecules themselves. Larger values of b are thus found for larger molecules. Numerical values for a are generally much larger than those for b.

Example: Find the correction in pressure necessary for the deviation from ideality for 1 mole of ammonia in a 1 liter flask at 0°C. (For NH_3, a = 4.2, b = 0.037)

Solution: According to the ideal gas law,

$P = nRT/V = (1)(0.0821)(273)/(1) = 22.4$ atm, while according to the van der Waals equation,

$$P = \frac{nRT}{(V - nb)} - \frac{n^2a}{V^2} = \frac{(1)(0.821)(273)}{(1 - 0.037)} - \frac{1^2(4.2)}{1}$$

$$= 23.3 - 4.2 = 19.1 \text{ atm}$$

The pressure is thus 3.3 atm less than would be predicted from the ideal gas law, or an error of 15 percent.

MCAT Expertise

Be familiar with the concepts embodied by this equation, but do not spend too much time working with it or memorizing it as it is not likely to be tested directly on the MCAT.

Note that including the correction term (a) has the effect of increasing the observed pressure (P) to that predicted by the ideal gas law.

Conclusion

In this chapter we reviewed the basic characteristics and behaviors of gases. The kinetic molecular theory of gases lays out the explanation for the behavior of ideal gases as described by the ideal gas law. The ideal gas law shows the mathematical relationship between four variables associated with gases: pressure, volume, temperature, and number of moles. We examined special cases of the ideal gas law in which temperature (Boyle's law) or pressure (Charles's law) is held constant. Boyle's law shows that when temperature is held constant there is an inverse relationship between pressure and volume. Charles's law shows that when pressure is held constant there is a direct relationship between temperature and volume. We also examined Dalton's law, which relates the partial pressure of a gas to its mole fraction and the sum of the partial pressures of all the gases in a system to the total pressure of the system. Finally, we examined the ways in which real gases deviate from the predicted behaviors of ideal gases. The van der Waals equation of state is a useful equation for correcting deviations based on molecular interactions and volumes.

From helium-filled balloons to the bubbles of carbon dioxide in a glass of soda, from the pressurized gases used for scuba diving to the air we breathe on land, gases are all around us. And yet, for all the different gases that bubble, flow, and settle in and through our daily living experiences, they behave in remarkably similar ways. Expect that the MCAT will treat gases with the level of attention that is appropriate to their importance in our physical lives.

CONCEPTS TO REMEMBER

- ☐ Gases are the least dense phase of matter. They are classified, along with liquids, as fluids because they flow in response to shearing forces and conform to the shape of their container. Unlike liquids, however, gases are compressible.

- ☐ The state of a gas system can be characterized by four properties: pressure, volume, temperature, and number of moles. Standard temperature and pressure (STP) is a set of conditions common in the study of gases; standard temperature is 273 K (0°C) and standard pressure is 1 atm.

- ☐ Ideal gases are described by the kinetic molecular theory of gases, which characterizes gases as composed of particles with negligible volume, no intermolecular forces, in continuous and random motion, undergoing elastic collisions with each other and the walls of their container, and having an average kinetic energy that is proportional to the temperature.

- ☐ Graham's law of diffusion and effusion states that for two or more gases at the same temperature, a gas with lower molar mass will diffuse or effuse more rapidly than a gas with higher molar mass.

- ☐ Regardless of chemical identity, equal amounts of gases occupy the same volume if they are at the same temperature and pressure. For example, one mole of any gas occupies 22.4 liters at STP.

- ☐ The ideal gas law, $PV = nRT$, describes the mathematical relationship between the four variables of the gas state for an ideal gas.

- ☐ Boyle's law is a special case of the ideal gas law for which temperature is held constant; it shows an inverse relationship between pressure and volume.

- ☐ Charles's law is a special case of the ideal gas law for which pressure is held constant; it shows a direct relationship between temperature and volume.

- ☐ Dalton's law of partial pressure states that the individual gas components of a mixture of gases will exert individual pressures, called partial pressures, in proportion to their mole fractions. The total pressure of a mixture of gases is equal to the sum of the individual partial pressures of the individual gas components.

- ☐ The behavior of real gases deviates from that predicted by the ideal gas law, especially under conditions of very high pressure or very low temperature. The van der Waals equation of state is used to correct for deviations due to intermolecular attractions and molecular volumes.

EQUATIONS TO REMEMBER

- [ ] $KE = \dfrac{1}{2mv^2} = \dfrac{3}{2kT}$

- [ ] $u_{rms} = \left(\dfrac{3RT}{MM}\right)^{1/2}$

- [ ] $\dfrac{r_1}{r_2} = \left(\dfrac{MM_2}{MM_1}\right)^{1/2} = \sqrt{\left(\dfrac{MM_2}{MM_1}\right)}$

- [ ] $PV = nRT$

- [ ] $d = \dfrac{m}{V} = \dfrac{P(MM)}{RT}$

- [ ] $PV = k$ or $P_1V_1 = P_2V_2$

- [ ] $\dfrac{V}{T} = k$ or $\dfrac{V_1}{T_1} = \dfrac{V_2}{T_2}$

- [ ] $P_A = P_T X_A$

- [ ] $\left(P + \dfrac{n^2a}{V^2}\right)(V - nb) = nRT$

Practice Questions

1. Based on your knowledge of gases, what conditions would be least likely to result in ideal gas behavior?

   A. High pressure and low temperature
   B. Low temperature and large volume
   C. High pressure and large volume
   D. Low pressure and high temperature

2. Calculate the density of neon gas at STP in g L^{-1}. The molar mass of neon can be approximated to 20.18 g mol^{-1}.

   A. 452.3 g L^{-1}
   B. 226.0 g L^{-1}
   C. 1.802 g L^{-1}
   D. 0.9009 g L^{-1}

3. A leak of helium gas through a small hole occurs at a rate of 3.22×10^{-5} mol s^{-1}. Compare the leakage rates of neon and oxygen gases to helium at the same temperature and pressure.

   A. Neon will leak faster than helium; oxygen will leak slower than helium.
   B. Neon will leak faster than helium; oxygen will leak slower than helium.
   C. Neon will leak slower than helium; oxygen will leak slower than helium.
   D. Neon will leak slower than helium; oxygen will leak faster than helium.

4. A 0.040 gram piece of magnesium is placed in a beaker of hydrochloric acid. Hydrogen gas is generated according to the following equation:

   $$Mg\ (s) + 2HCl\ (aq)\ MgCl_2\ (aq) + H_2\ (g)$$

   The gas is collected over water at 25°C, and the pressure during the experiment reads 784 mm Hg. The gas displaces a volume of 100 mL. The vapor pressure of water at 25°C is approximately 24.0 mm Hg. From this data, calculate how many moles of hydrogen are produced.

   A. 4.22×10^{-3} moles hydrogen
   B. 4.08×10^{-3} moles hydrogen
   C. 3.11 moles hydrogen
   D. 3.20 moles hydrogen

5. The properties of ideal gases state that ideal gases:

   I. have no volume.
   II. have no attractive forces between them.
   III. have no mass.

   A. I, II, and III
   B. I only
   C. I and II only
   D. I and III only

6. An 8.01 g sample of NH_4NO_3 (s) is placed into an evacuated 10.00 L flask and heated to 227°C. After the NH_4NO_3 totally decomposes, what is the approximate pressure in the flask?

$$NH_4NO_3 \, (s) \; N_2O \, (g) + H_2O \, (g)$$

A. 0.600 atm
B. 0.410 atm
C. 1.23 atm
D. 0.672 atm

7. The kinetic molecular theory states that:

A. the average kinetic energy of a molecule of gas is directly proportional to the temperature of the gas in Kelvin.
B. collisions between gas molecules are inelastic.
C. elastic collisions result in a loss of energy.
D. all gas molecules have the same kinetic energy.

8. The plots of two gases at STP are shown below. One of the gases is 1.0 L of helium and the other is 1.0 L of bromine. Which plot corresponds to each gas and why?

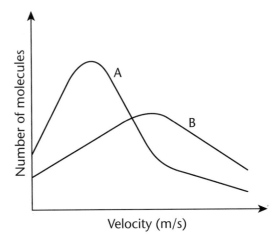

A. Curve A is helium and curve B is bromine because helium has a smaller molar mass than bromine.
B. Curve A is helium and curve B is bromine because the average kinetic energy of bromine is greater than the average kinetic energy of helium.
C. Curve A is bromine and curve B is helium because helium has a smaller molar mass than bromine.
D. Curve A is bromine and curve B is helium because the average kinetic energy of bromine is greater than the average kinetic energy of helium.

9. A balloon at standard temperature and pressure contains 0.20 moles of oxygen and 0.60 moles of nitrogen. What is the partial pressure of oxygen in the balloon?

   A. 0.20 atm
   B. 0.30 atm
   C. 0.60 atm
   D. 0.25 atm

10. The temperature at the center of the sun can be estimated based on the approximation that the gases at the center of the sun have an average molar mass equal to 2.00 g/mole. Approximate the temperature at the center of the sun using these additional values: the pressure equals 1.30×10^9 atm and the density at the center equals 1.20 g/cm³.

   A. 2.6×10^7 K
   B. 2.6×10^{10} K
   C. 2.6×10^4 K
   D. 2.6×10^6 K

11. The gaseous state of matter is characterized by the following properties:

   I. Gases are compressible.

   II. Gases assume the volume of their container.

   III. Gas particles exist as diatomic molecules.

   A. I and II only
   B. I and III only
   C. III only
   D. I, II, and III

12. A gas at a temperature of 27°C has a volume of 60.0 mL. What temperature change is needed to increase this gas to a volume of 90.0 mL?

   A. A reduction of 150°C
   B. An increase of 150°C
   C. A reduction of 40.5°C
   D. An increase of 40.5°C

13. A gaseous mixture contains nitrogen and helium and has a total pressure of 150 torr. The nitrogen particles comprise 80 percent of the gas and the helium particles make up the other 20 percent of the gas. What is the pressure exerted by each individual gas?

   A. 100 torr nitrogen, 50.0 torr helium
   B. 120 torr nitrogen, 30.0 torr helium
   C. 30.0 torr nitrogen, 150 torr helium
   D. 50.0 torr nitrogen, 100 torr helium

14. In which of the following situations is it impossible to predict how the pressure will change for a gas sample?

   A. The gas is cooled at a constant volume.
   B. The gas is heated at a constant volume.
   C. The gas is heated and the volume is simultaneously increased.
   D. The gas is cooled and the volume is simultaneously increased.

Small Group Questions

1. How does the addition or removal of gas B from a vessel affect the partial pressure of gas A?

2. Is hydrogen bonding present in steam?

Explanations to Practice Questions

1. A

Gases deviate from ideal behavior at higher pressures, which forces molecules closer together. The closer they are, the more they can participate in intermolecular forces, which violate the definition of an ideal gas. Similarly, low temperatures cause less space to exist between molecules. Less space makes the volume of the molecules more significant, causing the loss of another characteristic of an ideal gas. Answer choices that include the opposite, high temperature and low pressure, are incorrect because gases behave most ideally under these conditions. At high temperatures, molecules will move quickly and exhibit random motion and elastic collisions, which is a property of ideal gases. In an ideal gas it is assumed that there are no intermolecular attractions between gas molecules, which is valid at low pressures when there is ample space between them.

2. D

Density equals mass divided by volume. The mass of 1 mole of neon gas equals 20.18 grams. At STP, 1 mole of neon occupies 22.4 L. Dividing the mass, 20.18 grams, by the volume, 22.4 L, gives an approximate density of 0.9009 g L^{-1}.

3. C

Graham's law of effusion states that the relative rates of effusion of two gases at the same temperature and pressure are given by the inverse ratio of the square roots of the masses of the gas particles. In equation form, Graham's law can be represented by: $Rate_1/Rate_2 = \sqrt{(MM_2/MM_1)}$. If a molecule has a higher molecular weight, then it will leak at a slower rate than a gas with a lower molecular weight. Both neon and oxygen gases will leak at slower rates than helium because they both weigh more than helium.

4. B

The pressure of the gas is calculated by subtracting the vapor pressure of water from the measured pressure during the experiment: 784 mm Hg – 24 mm Hg = 760 mm Hg, or 1 atm. The ideal gas law can be used to calculate the moles of hydrogen gas. The volume of the gas equals 0.100 L, the temperatures equals 298 K, and R = 0.0821 (L atm / mol K). Solving the equation $PV = nRT$ for n gives 4.09×10^{-3} moles of hydrogen. (A) is incorrect and would result from mistakenly using 784 mm Hg of the pressure instead of the pressure adjusted for water vapor. (C) and (D) would both result from incorrectly using a pressure in mm Hg instead of converting to atm while using the gas constant R = 0.0821 (L atm / mol K).

5. C

Ideal gases are said to have no attractive forces between molecules. They are considered to have point masses, which theoretically take up no volume.

6. C

The first thing to do is balance the given chemical equation. The coefficients, from left to right, are 1, 1, and 2. The mass of solid, 8.01 grams, can be converted to moles of gas product by dividing by the molar mass of $NH_4NO_3(s)$ (80.06 g) and multiplying by the molar ratio of 3 moles of gas product to one mole of $NH_4NO_3(s)$. This gives approximately 0.300 moles of gas product. The ideal gas equation can be used to obtain the pressure in the flask. The values are as follows: R equals 0.0821 (L atm / mole K), the temperature in Kelvin is 500 K, and the volume is 10.00 L. Solving for P in the equation $PV = nRT$ gives a pressure of about 1.23 atm.

7. A

The average kinetic energy is directly proportional to the temperature of a gas in Kelvin. The kinetic molecular theory states that collisions between molecules are elastic, which do not result in a loss of energy. The kinetic energy of each gas molecule is not the same.

8. C

At STP, the difference between the distribution of velocities for helium and bromine gas is due to the difference in molar mass ($Rate_1/Rate_2$) = $\sqrt{(MM_2/MM_1)}$. Helium has a smaller molar mass than bromine. Particles with small masses travel faster than those with large masses, so the helium gas corresponds to curve B with higher velocities. (A) and (B) are incorrect because they inaccurately identify each curve on the graph. (D) is incorrect because the average kinetic energies of the gases cannot be determined with the given information.

9. D

At STP the pressure inside the balloon equals 1 atm. The total number of moles in the balloon equals 0.20 moles plus 0.60 moles, or 0.80 moles. P_{O_2} equals the mole fraction of oxygen (0.20/0.80) times the total pressure, 1 atm. The partial pressure of oxygen is 0.25 atm.

10. A

The ideal gas law can be modified to include density and determine the temperature of the sun.

n = mass/molecular weight

density (denoted D for this problem) = *mass*/V

The density is given in g/cm³ and must be converted to g/L so the units cancel in the above equation. Because 1 cm³ equals 1 mL and there are 1,000 mL in 1 L, the density can be multiplied by 1,000 to be converted to g/L.

$$PV = nRT$$

$$PV = \frac{(mass)RT}{MW}$$

$$T = \frac{PV(MW)}{R(mass)}$$

$$T = \frac{(P)(MW)}{(R)(D)}$$

$$= \frac{(1.3 \times 10^9 \text{ atm})(2 \text{ g/mol})}{(0.0821 \text{ atm L/mol K})(1.20 \text{ g/cm}^3)(1,000 \text{ cm}^3/\text{L})}$$

$$= 2.5 \times 10^7 \text{ K}$$

11. A

Gases are compressible, because they travel freely with large amounts of space between molecules. Because gas particles are far apart from each other and in rapid motion, they do tend to take up the volume of their container. There are many gases that exist as diatomic molecules (i.e., O_2, H_2, N_2) but this is not a property that characterizes all gases.

12. B

We will use $V_1/T_1 = V_2/T_2$. First we must convert the temperature to Kelvin by adding 273 to get 300 K as the initial temperature. Plugging into the equation and solving for T_2 gives 450 K. Subtracting the initial temperature, 300 K, gives an increase of 150 K. They are measured by the same increments, so an increase of 150 K corresponds to an increase of 150°C.

13. B

The partial pressure of each gas is found by multiplying the total pressure by the mole fraction of the gas. 80 percent of the molecules are nitrogen, so the mole fraction of nitrogen gas is equal to 0.80. Similarly, for helium the mole fraction is 0.20, because helium comprises 20 percent of the gas molecules. To find the pressure exerted by nitrogen, multiply the total pressure (150 torr) by 0.80 to obtain 120 torr of nitrogen. To find the pressure exerted by helium, multiply the total pressure by 0.20 to get 30 torr of helium.

14. C

Both a change in temperature and a change in volume can affect the gas's pressure. So, if one of those two variables is kept constant (i.e., (A) and (B)), we'll definitely be able to predict which way the pressure will change. At a constant volume, heating the gas will increase its pressure, and cooling the gas will decrease it. What about when both temperature and volume are changing? If they have the same effect on pressure, then we can still predict which way it will change. This is the case in (D). Cooling the gas and increasing its volume both decrease pressure. (C), on the other hand, presents us with too vague a scenario for us to definitively predict the change in pressure. Heating the gas would amplify the pressure, while increasing the volume would decrease it. Without knowing the magnitude of each specific influence, it's impossible to say whether the pressure would actually increase, decrease, or stay the same.

Phases and Phase Changes

Thwak! Thwak! "Stupid ketchup bottle! Why . . . won't you . . . come . . . out?!" Few things are more frustrating than ketchup that just refuses to budge. It usually happens with newly opened bottles, and the "stuck ketchup" phenomenon is so common that there's almost a ritualized nature to the process of getting it "unstuck": unscrew the top, turn the bottle on its side, and give it a few gentle shakes. If it doesn't come out right away, the next step is the administration of a few sturdy whacks with the palm of the hand against the bottom of the glass bottle. This is usually accompanied by some mild epithet suggestive of ketchup's alleged lack of intelligence (see quote above). More often than not, the physical abuse imposed upon the bottle only results in soft-tissue bruising and perhaps an alarming increase in the violent nature of the anti-ketchup epithets. Finally the ritual ends in an act of stabbing, and the evidence to convict is the spilled pool of red and the bloodred-coated butter knife that rests along the edge of the plate next to the pile of crispy french fries.

You can't really blame the ketchup, though. It doesn't know any better. In fact, it's only acting according to its nature as a member of a unique class of liquids called Bingham fluids. Bingham fluids do not begin to flow immediately upon application of shear stress. Unlike Newtonian fluids such as water or vegetable oil, which begin to flow as soon as a finite amount of shear stress is applied, Bingham fluids will only begin to flow when a minimum force value called the yield value is exceeded. Essentially, Bingham fluids behave like solids under static conditions and flow, as fluids, only when a shear stress at least equal to the yield value is applied. The sharp blows that you apply to the glass bottle of ketchup are usually strong enough to exceed ketchup's yield value. Unfortunately for the diner who ends up with a plate (and probably lap) flooded with ketchup, ketchup also belongs to a class of liquids known as pseudoplastic fluids, which demonstrate the property of shear-thinning. Shear-thinning liquids display reducing viscosity with increasing shear rate (related to fluid velocity). That ketchup is stuck, like a solid, in that bottle, until it isn't (because the yield value has been exceeded), at which point it begins to flow and the faster it flows, it "thins out" and becomes less viscous. The result is the mess on your plate and lap.

Our discussion in this chapter will focus on the three phases of matter, with particular emphasis on liquids and solids. The gaseous phase has been discussed extensively in the previous chapter. When the attractive forces between molecules (i.e., van der Waals forces, etc.) overcome the kinetic energy that keeps them apart in the gas phase, the molecules move closer together, entering the liquid or solid phase. The liquid and solid phases are often referred to as the condensed phases because of their higher densities compared to that of the gaseous phase. Molecules in the liquid and solid phases have lower degrees of freedom of movement than those in the gaseous phase as a result of the stronger intermolecular forces that dominate in the liquid and solid phases. After characterizing fluids and solids, we will review phase equilibria and phase diagrams. We will conclude our consideration of the phases of matter by reviewing the colligative properties of solutions.

Solids

We recognize **solids** by their rigidity and resistance to flow. The intermolecular attractive forces between the atoms, ions, or molecules of the solid matter hold them in a rigid arrangement. Although particles in the solid phase do not demonstrate linear motion, this does not mean that they do not possess any kinetic energy. The motion of particles in the solid phase, however, is mostly limited to vibration. As a result, solids have definite shapes (usually independent of the shape of a container) and volumes. Note that on the MCAT, solids (and liquids, for that matter) are considered to be incompressible; that is, a given mass of any solid or liquid will have a constant volume regardless of changes in pressure.

For most substances, the solid phase is the densest phase. A notable, and tested, exception to this generalization is water. Water in its solid phase (ice) is less dense than it is in its liquid phase, due to the larger spacing between the molecules in the crystalline structure of ice. The spacious lattice of ice crystals is stabilized by the hydrogen bonds between water molecules. Water molecules in the liquid phase also interact through hydrogen bonds, but because the water molecules are moving around, the lattice arrangement is absent and the molecules are able to move closer to each other. In fact, water's density reaches a maximum around 4°C. The density decreases at temperatures above 4°C because the increasing kinetic energy of the water molecules causes the molecules to move further apart. Between 4°C and 0°C, the density decreases because the lattice organization of hydrogen bonds is beginning to form.

The molecular arrangement of particles in the solid phase can be either **crystalline** or **amorphous.** Crystalline solids, such as the ionic compounds (e.g., NaCl), possess an ordered structure; their atoms exist in a specific three-dimensional geometric arrangement or lattice with repeating patterns of atoms, ions, or molecules. Amorphous solids, such as glass, plastic, and candle wax lack an ordered three-dimensional arrangement. The particles of amorphous solids are also fixed in place but not in the lattice arrangement that characterizes crystalline solids. Most solids are crystalline in structure. The two most common forms of crystals are metallic and ionic crystals.

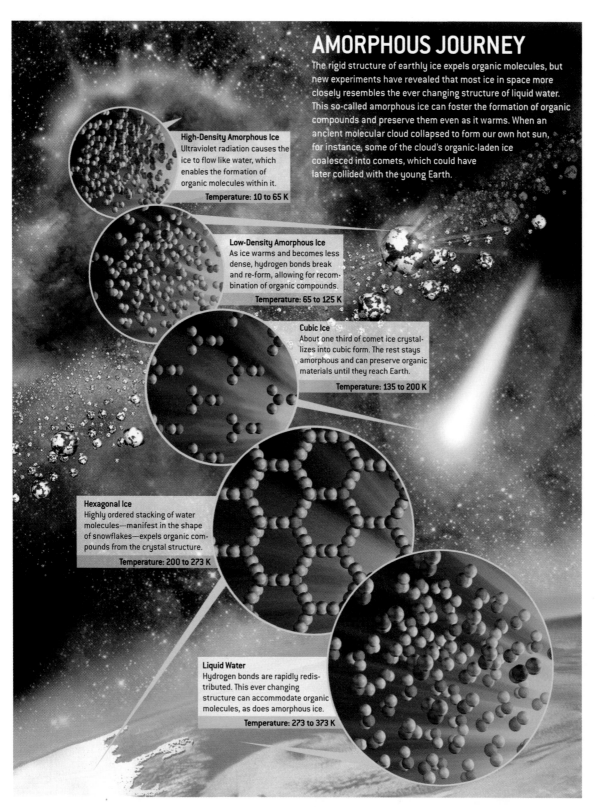

AMORPHOUS JOURNEY

The rigid structure of earthly ice expels organic molecules, but new experiments have revealed that most ice in space more closely resembles the ever changing structure of liquid water. This so-called amorphous ice can foster the formation of organic compounds and preserve them even as it warms. When an ancient molecular cloud collapsed to form our own hot sun, for instance, some of the cloud's organic-laden ice coalesced into comets, which could have later collided with the young Earth.

High-Density Amorphous Ice
Ultraviolet radiation causes the ice to flow like water, which enables the formation of organic molecules within it.
Temperature: 10 to 65 K

Low-Density Amorphous Ice
As ice warms and becomes less dense, hydrogen bonds break and re-form, allowing for recombination of organic compounds.
Temperature: 65 to 125 K

Cubic Ice
About one third of comet ice crystallizes into cubic form. The rest stays amorphous and can preserve organic materials until they reach Earth.
Temperature: 135 to 200 K

Hexagonal Ice
Highly ordered stacking of water molecules—manifest in the shape of snowflakes—expels organic compounds from the crystal structure.
Temperature: 200 to 273 K

Liquid Water
Hydrogen bonds are rapidly redistributed. This ever changing structure can accommodate organic molecules, as does amorphous ice.
Temperature: 273 to 373 K

Figure 8.1

Ionic solids are aggregates of positively and negatively charged ions that repeat according to defined patterns of alternating cations and anions. As a result, the solid mass of a compound, such as NaCl, does not contain discrete molecules (see Chapter 4, Compounds and Stoichiometry). The physical properties of ionic solids include high melting points, high boiling points, and poor electrical conductivity in the solid state but high conductivity in the molten state or in aqueous solution. These properties are due to the compounds' strong electrostatic interactions, which also cause the ions to be relatively immobile in the solid phase. Ionic structures are given by empirical formulas that describe the ratio of atoms in the lowest possible whole numbers. For example, the empirical formula $BaCl_2$ gives the ratio of barium to chloride atoms within the crystal.

Metallic solids consist of metal atoms packed together as closely as possible. Metallic solids have high melting and boiling points as a result of their strong covalent attractions. Pure metallic masses (consisting of a single metal element) are usually described as layers of spheres of roughly similar radii, stacked layer upon layer in a "staggered" arrangement such that one sphere in one layer fits into the indented space between the spheres that sit above and below it. These staggered arrangements (body-centered cubic and face-centered cubic, see below) are more common than layers of spheres stacked to form perfectly aligned columns of spheres (see simple cubic, below), because the staggered arrangement minimizes the separation between the atoms.

The repeating units of crystals (both ionic and metallic) are represented by **unit cells.** There are many types of unit cells. Chapter 4, Compounds and Stoichiometry, referred to the geometric arrangement of Na^+ and Cl^- ions in table salt as 6:6 coordinated, meaning that each sodium ion is surrounded by (coordinated by) six chloride ions, and each chloride ion is surrounded by (coordinated by) six sodium ions. This particular arrangement is also known as face-centered cubic. There are three **cubic unit cells** and you should recognize these for the MCAT: **simple cubic, body-centered cubic,** and **face-centered cubic.** Figure 8.2 illustrates these unit cells as ball-and-stick models.

simple cubic

body-centered cubic

face-centered cubic

Figure 8.2

In the ball-and-stick models illustrated, the anions are represented as small spheres separated by a lot of space, but more accurately, the spheres are packed quite closely. Figure 8.3 illustrates this. In the ionic unit cell, the spheres represent the anions; the spaces between the anions are occupied by the smaller cations. In most ionic compounds, the anion, which has gained one or more electrons, is much larger than the cation, which has lost one or more electrons. (The cations are *not* shown in Figures 8.2 and 8.3.)

simple cubic   body-centered cubic   face-centered cubic

Figure 8.3

Liquids

★★☆☆☆

The **liquid phase,** along with the solid phase, is considered a condensed phase because the spacing between the particles is reduced in comparison to that between gas particles. Furthermore, we assume that liquids, like solids, are incompressible, meaning that their volumes do not change in any significant way as a result of moderate pressure changes. But don't let all this talk of liquid as a "condensed phase" mislead you: there is still a lot of space separating liquid particles. You can "observe" this space for yourself through a very simple experiment. Fill a glass with very hot tap water all the way to the top of the glass, making sure that the water surface is actually "bulging" up above the level of the rim of the glass. Carefully add powdered sugar, by the teaspoon, to the water. Do not allow the spoon to touch the surface of the water and do not stir the solution. The hot water will dissolve the sugar on its own. Repeat the process. You will be able to add several teaspoons of sugar to the water before it spills out of the cup. The sugar dissolved into the empty spaces that separate water molecules!

Liquids are categorized as **fluids** (along with gases) because they do not resist shearing forces and flow when subjected to them. They also conform to the shapes of their containers. These behaviors are a result of the high degree of freedom of movement liquids possess. Like gas molecules, liquid molecules can move about in random motion and are disordered in their arrangement. Both liquids and gases are able to diffuse. Liquid molecules near the surface of the liquid can gain enough kinetic energy to escape into the gas phase; this is called evaporation.

One of the most important properties of liquids is their ability to mix—both with each other and with other phases—to form solutions (see Chapter 9, Solutions). The degree to which two liquids can mix is called their **miscibility.** While ethanol and water are completely **miscible,** oil and water are almost completely **immiscible**; that is, their molecules tend to repel each other due to their polarity differences. You're certainly familiar with the phrase, "Like dissolves like." Oil and water normally form separate layers when mixed, with the oil layer above the water because it is less dense. Organic chemistry takes advantage of the solubility differences of immiscible liquids to separate compounds through the method of liquid-liquid extraction. Agitation of two immiscible liquids can result in the formation of a fairly homogenous mixture called an **emulsion.** Although they look like solutions, emulsions are actually mixtures of discrete particles too small to be seen distinctly. Shaking a cruet of extra virgin olive oil and balsamic vinegar, seasoned with sea salt and fresh ground pepper, makes for a simple but delicious emulsion for your mixed baby greens salad.

Phase Equilibria

In an isolated system, **phase changes** (solid ↔ liquid ↔ gas) are reversible, and equilibrium of phases will eventually be reached. For example, at 1 atm and 0°C in an isolated system, an ice cube and the water in which it is floats are in equilibrium. In other words, some of the ice may absorb heat (from the liquid water) and melt, but since that heat is being removed from the liquid water, an equal amount of the liquid water will freeze and form ice. Thus, the relative amounts of ice and water remain constant. Equilibrium between the liquid and gas states of water will be established in a closed container such as a plastic water bottle with the cap screwed on tightly. At room temperature and atmospheric pressure most of the water in the bottle will be in the liquid phase, but a small number of molecules at the surface will gain enough kinetic energy to escape into the gas phase; likewise, a small number of gas molecules will lose sufficient kinetic energy to re-enter the liquid phase. After a while, equilibrium is established and the relative amounts of water in the liquid and gas phases become constant—at room temperature and atmospheric pressure, equilibrium occurs when the air above the water has about 3 percent humidity. Phase equilibria are analogous to the dynamic equilibria of reversible chemical reactions for which the concentrations of reactants and products are constant because the rates of the forward and reverse reactions are equal.

GAS-LIQUID EQUILIBRIUM

The temperature of any substance in any phase is related to the average kinetic energy of the molecules that make up the substance. However, as we saw in Chapter 7, not all the molecules have exactly the same instantaneous speeds and therefore the molecules possess a range of instantaneous kinetic energy values. In the liquid phase, the molecules have relatively large degrees of freedom of movement. Some of the molecules near the surface of the liquid may have enough kinetic energy to leave the liquid phase and escape into the gaseous phase. This process is known as **evaporation** (or **vaporization**). Each time the liquid loses a high-energy particle, the temperature of the remaining liquid decreases. Evaporation is an endothermic process, for which the heat source is the liquid water. Of course, the liquid water itself may be receiving thermal energy from some other source, as in the case of a puddle of water drying up under the hot summer sun or a pot of water on the stovetop. Given enough energy, the liquid will completely evaporate.

In covered or closed container, the escaping molecules are trapped above the solution. These molecules exert a countering pressure, which forces some of the gas back into the liquid phase; this process is called **condensation.** Condensation is facilitated by lower temperature or higher pressure. Atmospheric pressure acts on a liquid in a manner similar to that of an actual physical lid. As evaporation and condensation proceed, the respective rates of the two processes become equal and equilibrium is reached. The pressure that the gas exerts over the liquid at equilibrium is the vapor pressure of the liquid. Vapor pressure increases as temperature increases, since more molecules have sufficient kinetic energy to escape into the gas phase. The temperature at which the vapor pressure of the liquid equals the ambient (also known as external, applied, or atmospheric) pressure is called the **boiling point.** At boiling, vaporization happens throughout the entire volume of the liquid, not just near its surface. The bubbles of gas that rise from your pot of boiling pasta water are gaseous water molecules, plus the small amounts of atmospheric gases (mostly nitrogen and oxygen gas) that had been dissolved in the water.

LIQUID-SOLID EQUILIBRIUM

We've already illustrated the equilibrium that can exist between the liquid and the solid phases of water at 0°C. Even though the atoms or molecules of a solid are confined to definite locations, each atom or molecule can undergo motions about some equilibrium position. These vibrational motions increase when heat is applied. From our understanding of entropy, we can say that the availability of energy microstates increases as the temperature of the solid increases. In basic terms, this means that the molecules have greater freedom of movement and energy disperses. If atoms or molecules in the solid phase absorb enough energy, the three-dimensional structure of the solid will break down and the atoms or molecules will escape into the liquid phase. The transition from solid to liquid is called **fusion** or **melting.** The reverse process, from liquid to solid, is called **solidification, crystallization,** or **freezing.** The temperature at which these processes occur is called the melting point or freezing point, depending on the direction of the transition. Whereas pure crystalline solids have distinct, very sharp melting points, amorphous solids, such as glass, plastic, and candle wax, tend to melt (or solidify) over a larger range of temperatures, due to their less-ordered molecular distribution. One of the surest signs that a dinner party has come to its natural and necessary conclusion is when the dinner guests start playing with the liquid wax dripping down the side of the candlesticks, allowing it to cool and solidify on their fingertips.

GAS-SOLID EQUILIBRIUM

The final phase equilibrium is that which exists between the gas and solid phase. When a solid goes directly into the gas phase, the process is called **sublimation.** Dry ice (solid CO_2) sublimes at room temperature and atmospheric pressure; the absence of the liquid phase makes it a convenient refrigerant and a fun addition to punch bowls at parties. The reverse transition, from the gaseous to the solid phase, is called **deposition.** In organic chemistry, a device known as the cold finger (the name sounds more malicious than it actually is) is used to purify a product that is heated under reduced pressure to cause it to sublimate. The desired product is usually more volatile than the impurities, so the gas is purer than the original product and the impurities are left in the solid state. The gas then deposits onto the cold finger, which has cold water flowing through it, yielding a purified solid product that can be collected. Another common instance of sublimation is "freezer burn" on meats and vegetables that are stored for long periods of time in the freezer. The frozen water in the meat or vegetables will slowly sublimate over time and what is left is fit only for the garbage. On the other hand, sublimation is used to produce freeze-dried foods, such as coffee, "emergency survival meals," and perhaps most (in)famously, astronaut ice cream. The crackly frost of late autumn mornings in colder climates is formed by deposition of water vapor in the air.

THE GIBBS FUNCTION

As with all equilibria, the thermodynamic criterion for each of the phase equilibria is that the change in Gibbs free energy must be equal to zero ($\Delta G = 0$). For an equilibrium between a gas and a solid:

$$\Delta G = G(g) - G(s) = 0$$

therefore $\qquad G(g) = G(s)$

The same is true of the Gibbs functions for any other phase equilibria.

HEATING CURVES

When a compound is heated, the temperature rises until the melting or boiling points are reached. Then the temperature remains constant as the compound is converted to the next phase, i.e., liquid or gas, respectively. Once the entire sample is converted, then the temperature begins to rise again. See the heating curves depicted in Figure 8.4.

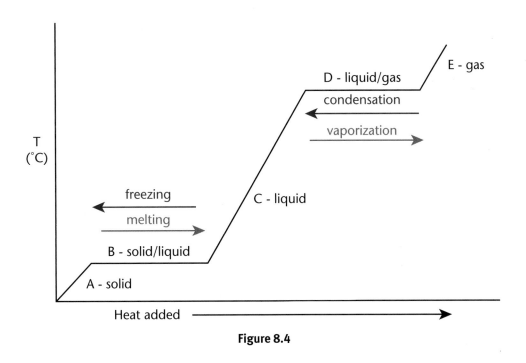

Figure 8.4

Phase Diagrams ★★☆☆☆

Key Concept

Every pure substance has a characteristic phase diagram.

Phase diagrams are graphs that show the temperatures and pressures at which a substance will be thermodynamically stable in a particular phase. They also show the temperatures and pressures at which phases will be in equilibrium.

SINGLE COMPONENT

The phase diagram for a single compound is shown in Figure 8.5.

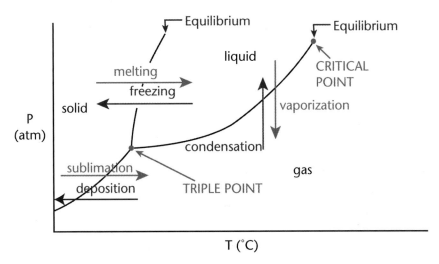

Figure 8.5

Real World

Because of H_2O's unique properties, ice floats and ice skates flow smoothly over ice. This all "boils" down to the negative slope of the solid-liquid equilibrium line in its phase diagram. Because the density of ice is less than that of liquid H_2O, an increase in pressure (at a constant temperature) will actually melt ice (the opposite of the substance seen in Figure 8.5).

The lines on a phase diagram are called the **lines of equilibrium** or the **phase boundaries** and indicate the temperature and pressure values for the equilibria between phases. The lines of equilibrium divide the diagram into three regions corresponding to the three phases—solid, liquid, and gas—and they themselves represent the phase transformations. Line A represents crystallization/fusion, line B vaporization/condensation, and line C sublimation/deposition. In general, the gas phase is found at high temperatures and low pressures; the solid phase is found at low temperatures and high pressures; and the liquid phase is found at moderate temperatures and moderate pressures. The point at which the three phase boundaries meet is called the **triple point.** This is the temperature and pressure at which the three phases exist in equilibrium. The phase boundary that separates the solid and the liquid phases extends indefinitely from the triple point. The phase boundary between the liquid and gas phases, however, terminates at a point called the critical point. This is the temperature and pressure above which there is no distinction between the phases. Although this may seem to be an impossibility—after all, it's possible always to distinguish between the liquid and the solid phase—such "supercritical fluids" are perfectly logical. As a liquid is heated in a closed system its density decreases and the density of the vapor sitting above it increases. The critical point is the temperature and pressure at which the two densities become equal and there is no distinction between the two phases. The heat of vaporization at this point and for all temperatures and pressures above the critical point values is zero. So, it's certainly possible to create a supercritical fluid, but definitely not common (in everyday life). We can assure you that none of you have ever come close to approaching, say, the critical point temperature and pressure for water no matter how much "industrial strength" your high-pressure home espresso machine possesses: 647 K (374°C or 705°F) and 22.064 MPa (218 atm).

A triple-point cell is a vacuum-tight flask containing water vapor, liquid water and an ice mantle that has formed around an inner test tube.

Test Tube
Rubber Stopper
Electrical Tape
Water Vapor
Water
Water-Alcohol Mixture
Ice Mantle
Flask

Figure 8.6

MULTIPLE COMPONENTS

The phase diagram for a mixture of two or more components is complicated by the requirement that the composition of the mixture, as well as the temperature and pressure, must be specified. For example, consider a solution of two liquids, A and B. The vapor above the solution is a mixture of the vapors of A and B. The pressures exerted by vapor A and vapor B on the solution are the vapor pressures that each exerts above its individual liquid phase. Raoult's law enables one to determine the relationship between the vapor pressure of gaseous A and the concentration of liquid A in the solution.

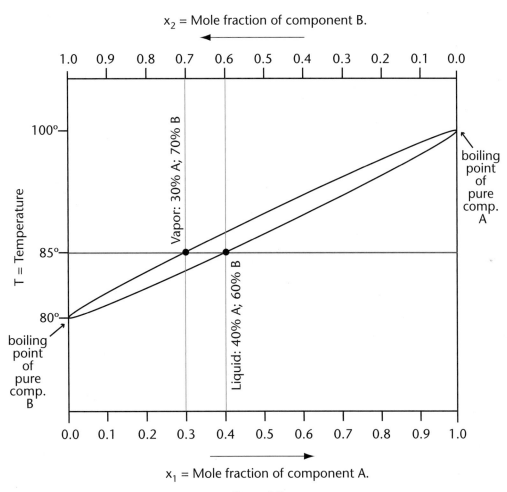

Figure 8.7

Curves such as this show the different compositions of the liquid phase and the vapor phase above a solution for different temperatures. The upper curve is the composition of the vapor, while the lower curve is that of the liquid. It is this difference in composition that forms the basis of distillation, an important separation technique in organic chemistry. For example, if we were to start with a mixture of A and B at a proportion of 40 percent A and 60 percent B and heat it to that solution's boiling point (85°C), the resulting vapor would not have the same composition as the liquid solution because the two compounds have different volatilities. Compound B is more volatile because it has the lower boiling point. Therefore, vapor B should be in larger proportion to vapor A, compared to the proportion of B to A in the liquid phase. Because the boiling point temperature for this 60–40 mixture is 85°C, the vapor will also be at 85°C. At this temperature, we can tell from the graph that the vapor composition will be 30 percent A and 70 percent B. Indeed, the proportion of the more volatile compound, in this case compound B, has been enhanced. Repeated rounds of boiling (vaporization) and condensation will ultimately yield a pure sample of compound B.

Colligative Properties

All the way back at the start of this book, we suggested that adding salt to water will yield a solution whose boiling point is higher than that of the pure water. While this is a true statement, we also suggested that the quantity of salt that is normally added to a pot of cooking water is not sufficient to cause a significant rise in the boiling point or a significant decrease in the cooking time. In culinary practice, adding salt to your cooking water merely (but importantly) contributes to the flavor of the food. The measurable change in boiling point of a solution compared to that of the pure solvent is one of the **colligative properties** of solutions. The colligative properties are physical properties of solutions that are dependent upon the concentration of dissolved particles but not upon the chemical identity of the dissolved particles. These properties—vapor pressure depression, boiling point elevation, freezing point depression, and osmotic pressure—are usually associated with dilute solutions (see Chapter 9, Solutions).

VAPOR PRESSURE DEPRESSION

When you add solute to a solvent and the solute dissolves, the solvent in solution has a vapor pressure that is lower than the vapor pressure of the pure solvent for all temperatures. For example, consider compound A in Figure 8.7. Compound A in its pure form (mole fraction = 1.0) has a boiling point of 100°C. Based on this information alone we can assume that compound A is water. Compound B, which is more volatile than water and boils, in pure form (mole fraction = 1.0), at around 80°C could be ethanol, which has a boiling point of 78.3°C. When a small amount of ethanol is added to water to create a dilute solution, say 90 percent water and 10 percent alcohol, the boiling point is around 95°C and the vapor composition above the solution will be about 80 percent water and 20 percent ethanol. The relative decrease in the proportion of water in the vapor above the dilute water-alcohol solution is related to the decrease in the vapor pressure of water above the solution.

If the vapor pressure of A above pure solvent A is designated by P°_A and the vapor pressure of A above the solution containing B is P_A, the vapor pressure decreases as follows:

$$\Delta P = P^\circ_A - P_A$$

In the late 1800s, the French chemist François Marie Raoult determined that this vapor pressure decrease is also equivalent to:

$$\Delta P = X_B P^\circ_A$$

where X_B is the mole fraction of the solute B in solution with solvent A. Because $X_B = 1 - X_A$ and $\Delta P = P^\circ_A - P_A$, substitution into the previous equation leads to the common form of **Raoult's law**:

$$P_A = X_A P^\circ_A$$

where X_A is the mole fraction of the solvent A in the solution. Similarly, the expression for the vapor pressure of the solute in solution (assuming it is volatile) is given by:

$$P_B = X_B P^\circ_B$$

Raoult's law holds only when the attraction between the molecules of the different components of the mixture is equal to the attraction between the molecules of any one component in its pure state. When this condition does not hold, the relationship between mole fraction and vapor pressure will deviate from Raoult's law. Solutions that obey Raoult's law are called **ideal solutions.**

BOILING POINT ELEVATION

When a nonvolatile solute is dissolved into a solvent to create a solution, the boiling point of the solution will be greater than that of the pure solvent. Earlier we defined the boiling point as the temperature at which the vapor pressure of the liquid equals the ambient (external) pressure. We've just seen that adding solute to a solvent results in a decrease in the vapor pressure of the solvent in the solution at all temperatures. If the vapor pressure of a solution is lower than that of the pure solvent, then more energy (and consequently a higher temperature) will be required before its vapor pressure equals the ambient pressure. The extent to which the boiling point of a solution is raised relative to that of the pure solvent is given by the following formula:

$$\Delta T_b = i K_b m$$

where ΔT_b is the boiling point elevation, K_b is a proportionality constant characteristic of a particular solvent (and will be given to you on Test Day), m is the molality of the solution [molality = moles of solute per kilogram of solvent (mol/kg); see Chapter 9, Solutions] and i is the van't Hoff factor, which is the moles of particles dissolved into a solution per mole of solute molecules. For example, $i = 2$ for NaCl because each molecule of sodium chloride dissociates into two particles, a sodium ion and a chloride ion, when it dissolves.

FREEZING POINT DEPRESSION

The presence of solute particles in a solution interferes with the formation of the lattice arrangement of solvent molecules associated with the solid state. Thus, a greater amount of energy must be removed from the solution (resulting in a lower temperature) in order for the solution to solidify. For example, pure water freezes at 0°C, but for every mole of solute dissolved in 1 kg (1 liter) of water, the freezing point is lowered by 1.86°C. Therefore, the K_f for water is −1.86°C/m. As is the case for K_b, the values for K_f are unique to each solvent and will be given to you on Test Day. The formula for calculating the freezing point depression for a solution is:

$$\Delta T_f = i K_f m$$

where ΔT_f is the freezing point depression, K_f is the proportionality constant characteristic of a particular solvent, m is the molality of the solution, and i is the van't Hoff factor.

If you've ever wondered why we salt roads in the winter, this is why: the salt mixes with the snow and ice and initially dissolves into the small amount of liquid water that is in equilibrium with the solid phase (the snow and ice). The solute in solution causes a disturbance to the equilibrium such that the rate of melting is unchanged (because the salt can't interact with the solid water that is stabilized in a rigid lattice arrangement), but the rate of freezing is decreased (the solute displaces some of the water molecules from the solid-liquid interface and prevents liquid water from entering into the solid phase).

This imbalance causes more ice to melt than water to freeze. Melting is an endothermic process, so heat is initially absorbed from the liquid solution, causing the solution temperature to fall below the ambient temperature. Now, there is a temperature gradient and heat flows from the "warmer" air to the "cooler" aqueous solution; this additional heat facilitates more melting—even though the temperature of the solution is actually colder than it was before the solute was added! The more the ice melts into liquid water, the more the solute is dispersed through the liquid. The resulting salt solution, by virtue of the presence of the solute particles, has a lower freezing point than the pure water and remains in the liquid state even at temperatures that would normally cause pure water to freeze.

Could we use table sugar instead of salt? Absolutely—but sugar is more expensive. Could we use LiCl instead of NaCl? Absolutely—but NaCl is a lot easier and more economical. Besides, we've heard of manic drivers in need of a mood stabilizer, but manic roads? Could we use magical fairy dust? Absolutely—so long as magical fairy dust is soluble in water. In other words, it doesn't matter what the solute is. Freezing point depression is a colligative property that depends only upon the concentration of particles, not upon their identity.

OSMOTIC PRESSURE

One of the most important roles of the cell membrane is to maintain the unique differences between the intracellular and extracellular compartments. Both of these compartments are aqueous solutions separated by the cell membrane, which functions as a semipermeable barrier. Channels and pumps in the membrane serve to create and maintain concentration gradients of various solutes on either side of the membrane. A delicate balance of water influx and efflux must be established in order to prevent the cell from becoming dehydrated and shrinking or waterlogged and possibly bursting. The extracellular compartment itself is in continuity with the plasma compartment of the blood. A balance between these two compartments is dependent upon two pressures: the hydrostatic pressure of the blood generated by the contraction of the heart and the osmotic pressure of the plasma compartment primarily established by the concentration of plasma proteins such as albumin. (Since the osmotic pressure of the plasma compartment is based on the concentration of plasma protein, it is also called oncotic pressure.) The hydrostatic pressure tends to push fluid volume out of the vascular compartment into the extracellular compartment, while the osmotic pressure tends to pull fluid volume back into the vascular compartment from the extracellular compartment.

Consider a container separated into two compartments by a semipermeable membrane (which, by definition, selectively permits the passage of certain molecules). One compartment contains pure water, while the other contains water with dissolved solute. The membrane allows water but not solute to pass through. Because substances tend to flow, or diffuse, from higher to lower concentration (which results in an increase in entropy), water will diffuse from the compartment containing pure water into the compartment containing the water-solute mixture. This net flow will cause the water level in the compartment containing the solution to rise above the level in the compartment containing pure water.

Because the solute cannot pass through the membrane, the concentrations of solute in the two compartments can never be equal. However, the hydrostatic pressure exerted by the water level in the solute-containing compartment will eventually oppose the influx of water; thus, the water level will rise only to the point at which it exerts a sufficient pressure to counterbalance the tendency of water to flow across the membrane. This pressure is defined as the **osmotic pressure (Π)** of the solution, and is given by the formula:

$$\Pi = iMRT$$

> ### Bridge
> Osmosis explains how many biological systems regulate their fluid levels.

where M is the molarity of the solution, R is the ideal gas constant, T is the absolute temperature (in Kelvin), and i is the van't Hoff factor. The equation clearly shows that osmotic pressure is directly proportional to the molarity of the solution. Thus, osmotic pressure, like all colligative properties, depends only upon the presence of the solute, not its chemical identity.

One application of osmotic pressure is a particular method of water purification called reverse osmosis (RO). In reverse osmosis, impure water is placed into one container separated from another container by a semipermeable membrane. High pressure is applied to the impure water, which forces it to diffuse across the membrane, filling the compartment on the other side of the membrane with purified water. Because the water is being forced across the membrane in the direction opposite its concentration gradient (that is, the water is being forced from the compartment with the lower concentration of water to the compartment with the higher concentration of water), large pressures (higher than the solution's osmotic pressure) are needed to accomplish the purification.

Conclusion

In this chapter we have reviewed the important concepts and calculations related to the condensed phases of the solid and liquid states of matter. For solids, we learned that the organization of the particles is either in a three-dimensional lattice formation producing a crystalline structure or in a less-ordered arrangement described as amorphous. Ionic and metallic solids have crystalline structure, while glass, plastic, and candle wax have amorphous structure. There are many different ways in which the particles that make up a crystalline structure can be organized and the basic repeating unit of that organization is called the unit cell. We reviewed the three cubic unit cells. Liquids, like gases, are defined by their ability to flow in response to shearing forces. Liquids that can mix together are called miscible, while those that repel each other and separate into different layers, like oil and water, are called immiscible. We examined the equilibria that exist between the different phases, and noted that the change in Gibbs function for each phase change in equilibrium is zero, as is the case for all equilibria. Finally, we examined the colligative properties of solutions and the mathematics that govern them. The colligative properties—vapor pressure depression, boiling point elevation, freezing point depression, and osmotic pressure—are physical properties of solutions that depend upon the concentration of dissolved particles but not upon their chemical identity.

We concluded this chapter with an overview of the colligative properties of solutions; the next chapter will continue the review of the behaviors and characteristics of solutions and the mathematics of solution chemistry that will earn you points on Test Day.

CONCEPTS TO REMEMBER

☐ In the solid and liquid phases, the atoms, ions, or molecules are sufficiently condensed to allow the intermolecular forces, such as van der Waals, dipole-dipole and hydrogen bonds, to hold the particles together and restrict their degrees of freedom of movement.

☐ Solids are defined by their rigidity (ability to maintain a shape independent of a container) and resistance to flow.

☐ The molecular arrangement in solids can be either crystalline or amorphous. Crystalline structure is a three-dimensional lattice arrangement of repeating units called the unit cell. Amorphous solids lack this lattice arrangement.

☐ Liquids are defined as fluids because they flow in response to shearing forces and assume the shape of their container.

☐ Liquids like water and alcohol will mix together and are called miscible; liquids like water and oil will not mix together and are called immiscible. Agitation of immiscible liquids will result in an emulsion.

☐ Phase equilibria will exist at certain temperatures and pressures for each of the different phase changes: fusion (crystallization), vaporization (condensation), and sublimation (deposition).

☐ The change in Gibbs free energy for phase equilibria is zero.

☐ The phase diagram of a given system graphs the phases and phase equilibria as a function of temperature and pressure.

☐ The phase diagram for a solution consisting of multiple components will indicate the composition of the liquid and the vapor at different temperatures and pressures.

☐ The colligative properties—vapor pressure depression, boiling point elevation, freezing point depression, and osmotic pressure—are physical properties of solutions that depend upon the concentration of dissolved particles but not upon their chemical identity.

EQUATIONS TO REMEMBER

☐ $P_A = X_A P^o_A$

☐ $\Delta T_b = i K_b m$

☐ $\Delta T_f = i K_f m$

☐ $\Pi = i M R T$

Practice Questions

1. Which of the following substances is illustrated by the phase diagram in the figure below?

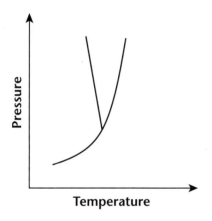

   A. CO_2
   B. NaCl
   C. Ne
   D. H_2O

2. Which of the following proportionalities best describes the relationship between the number of intermolecular forces and heat of vaporization for a given substance?

   A. They are proportional.
   B. They are inversely proportional.
   C. Their relationship cannot be generalized.
   D. There is no relationship between them.

3. Which of the following molecules is likely to have the highest melting point?

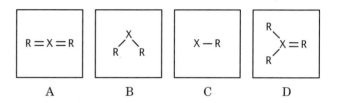

   A   B   C   D

4. Which of the following physical conditions favor a gaseous state for most substances?

   A. High pressure and high temperature
   B. Low pressure and low temperature
   C. High pressure and low temperature
   D. Low pressure and high temperature

5. Which of the following explanations best describes the mechanism by which solute particles affect the melting point of ice?

   A. Melting point elevates because the kinetic energy of the substance increases.
   B. Melting point elevates because the kinetic energy of the substance decreases.
   C. Melting point depresses because solute particles interfere with lattice formation.
   D. Melting point depresses because solute particles enhance lattice formation.

6. In the figure below, which phase change is represented by the arrow?

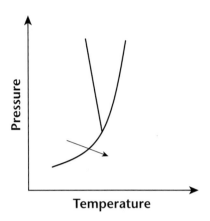

A. Condensation
B. Deposition
C. Sublimation
D. Vaporization

7. Which of the following situations would most favor the change of water from a liquid to a solid?

  I. Decreased solute concentration of a substance

  II. Decreased temperature of a substance

  III. Decreased pressure on a substance

A. I only
B. II only
C. I and II only
D. II and III only

8. The heats of vaporization of four substances are given in the table below. Which of these substances has the lowest boiling point?

Comparative Heats of Vaporization

Liquid	Heat Required (cal/g)
Chlorine	67.4
Ether	9.4
Carbon dioxide	72.2
Ammonia	295

A. Chlorine
B. Ether
C. Carbon dioxide
D. Ammonia

9. What factor(s) determine whether or not two liquids are miscible?

A. Molecular size
B. Molecular polarity
C. Density
D. Both B and C

10. Alloys are mixtures of new metals in either the liquid or solid phase. Which of the following is usually true of alloys?

A. The melting/freezing point of an alloy will be lower than that of either of the component metals because the new bonds are stronger.

B. The melting/freezing point of an alloy will be lower than that of either of the component metals because the new bonds are weaker.

C. The melting/freezing point of an alloy will be greater than that of either of the component metals because the new bonds are weaker.

D. The melting/freezing point of an alloy will be greater than that of either of the component metals because the new bonds are stronger.

11. The osmotic pressure at STP of a solution made from 1 L of NaCl (aq) containing 117 g of NaCl is

A. 44.77 atm.

B. 48.87 atm.

C. 89.54 atm.

D. 117 atm.

Small Group Questions

1. On water's pressure-temperature phase diagram, the boundary between liquid and solid has a negative slope. Explain this phenomenon, focusing on how density affects pressure and temperature.

2. Which would have a greater effect on the boiling point of one liter of water: 2 moles of sodium nitrate or 1 mole of carbonic acid? What pieces of information do we need to calculate this answer?

Explanations to Practice Questions

1. D

For the scope of the MCAT, water is the only substance that has a solid/liquid equilibrium line with a negative slope. We are not expected to know specific phase diagrams for other compounds.

2. A

Intermolecular forces hold molecules closer to one another, which relates to the compound's phase. As there are more intermolecular forces, the amount of heat needed to change phase (such as in vaporization) increases as well, thus showing a proportional, positive relationship.

3. B

This molecule is likely to have unequal sharing of electrons, which means it will be polar. Polarity often leads to increased bonding because of the positive-negative attractive forces between molecules. Greater bonding or stronger intermolecular forces both lead to higher melting points because more heat is needed to break these interactions and cause liquefaction. (A) is nonpolar, making its intermolecular forces weaker than (B) or (C). (D) is only weakly polar, because the geometry of this molecule will make some of the polarized bonds cancel each other out. (C) will have some polarity, but less than (B) because only one bond is polarized.

4. D

We can imagine a high pressure situation as one in which molecules are in close proximity (low volume container) and forced to interact with one another. Intermolecular attractions are necessary in the solid and liquid phases, but assumed to be negligible in the gas phase. So, we can assume that high pressure is not conducive to the gaseous state. What about temperature? Because temperature is a measure of average kinetic energy of the molecules, an increase in the average kinetic energy increases molecules' ability to move apart from one other, ultimately entering a gaseous state. Decreasing the temperature (or kinetic energy) or increasing pressure both favor the more organized liquid and solid phases.

5. C

Melting point depresses upon solute addition, making (A) and (B) incorrect. Solute particles interfere with lattice formation, the highly organized state in which solid molecules align themselves. Colder than normal conditions are necessary to create the solid structure.

6. C

This answer choice shows movement from the solid to gas phase, which is, by definition, sublimation.

7. C

Both I and II are correct. Dissolved solutes interfere with the crystalline lattice bonds of a solid, and therefore favor the liquid side of the equilibrium. Conversely, a decreased amount of solute would favor a solid state (I). Additionally, decreased temperature (II) is a decrease in the average kinetic energy of the molecules, making lower-energy phases (i.e. solid) more likely to exist. Finally, decreasing pressure (III) would actually favor higher-energy phases (i.e., liquid or gas) over solids. The only answer choice that includes both I and II is (C).

8. B

(B) has the lowest heat required for vaporization, which by definition determines the boiling point or the lowest temperature required for phase change from liquid to gas. All of the other answer choices have higher heats of vaporization as seen in the table associated with the question.

9. B

The miscibility of two liquids strongly depends on their polarities. A polar liquid can mix with another polar liquid, and a nonpolar liquid can mix with another nonpolar liquid. In general, however, polar and nonpolar liquids are not miscible with each other. (A), molecular size, and (C), the density of a liquid, do not directly affect the miscibility (although (C) should remind you that two immiscible liquids will form separate layers, with the denser liquid on the bottom). Thus, (B) is the only correct choice.

10. B

The bonds between different metal atoms in an alloy are much weaker than those between the atoms in pure metals. Therefore, breaking these bonds requires less energy than does breaking the bonds in pure metals. The more stable the bonds are in a compound, the higher the melting and freezing points. They tend to be lower for alloys than for pure metals. Alternately, an alloy can be looked at as a solid solution; impurities lower the melting point.

11. C

The osmotic pressure (Π) of a solution is given by $\Pi = iMRT$. At STP, $T = 273$ K; R, the ideal gas constant, equals 8.2×10^{-2} L $\bullet$ atm/K $\bullet$ mol. To determine the molarity, find the formula weight of NaCl from the periodic table; FW = 58.5 g/mol. The number of moles in the solution described is:

$$\frac{117 \text{ g/L}}{58.5 \text{ g/mol}} = 2 \text{ mol undissociated NaCl/L}$$

However, because NaCl is a strong electrolyte, it will completely dissociate in aqueous solution, yielding 4 moles of particles per liter of solution, i.e., 2 moles of Na^+ and 2 moles of Cl^-. Thus:

$$\Pi = (4 \text{ mol/L})(8.2 \times 10^{-2} \text{ L} \bullet \text{atm/K} \bullet \text{mol})(273 \text{ K})$$
$$= 89.54 \text{ atm.}$$

Remember that colligative properties depend on the number of particles, not their identity.

9

Solutions

What do first aid instant cold packs and sweet tea have in common? Not much, you might think, but both, in fact, demonstrate the same principles of solution chemistry. Instant cold packs contain two compartments, one holding water and the other ammonium nitrate. When you bend the pack, the two compartments break open, allowing the ammonium nitrate to dissolve into the water. Sweet tea is made by dissolving a large amount of sugar into strongly brewed tea—the sweetest of the sweet teas may approach 22 brix, which means that in every 100 grams of tea, there are 22 grams of sugar. (As a point of reference, this is about twice the sweetness of regular cola.) When the ammonium nitrate or the sugar dissolves in the water to produce the respective solutions, three events must take place. First, the intermolecular interactions between the molecules of ammonium nitrate (or between the sugar molecules) must be broken. Second, the intermolecular interactions between the molecules of water must be broken. Third, new intermolecular interactions between the ammonium nitrate and the water molecules (or between the sugar and the water) must be formed.

We know from our discussion in Chapter 3, Bonding and Chemical Interactions, that energy is required to break these intermolecular interactions and that energy is released when new ones are formed. For the creation of both the ammonium nitrate and sugar solutions, more energy is needed to break the original intermolecular interactions than is released when new intermolecular interactions are formed. Thus, the creation of both of these solutions is an endothermic process. Now, the formation of the ammonium nitrate solution is much more endothermic than the formation of the sugar solution. And this is why ammonium nitrate is useful in instant cold packs. When it dissolves in water, the system must absorb an amount of energy equal to 6.14 kcal/mol of ammonium nitrate. The heat is absorbed from the surrounding environment and the pack feels cool to the touch.

Although the dissolution of sugar into water is not as strongly endothermic, we nevertheless have an intuitive understanding of the process's endothermicity because we all know that the easiest way to dissolve lots of sugar into water (such as tea or coffee) is to heat up the water and then add the sugar. Because heating the water increases the solubility of sugar, it must be that the dissolution of sugar into water is an endothermic process (think application of Le Châtelier's principle and changes in temperature, Chapter 5, Chemical Kinetics and Equilibrium).

In this chapter, our focus will be on the characteristics and behaviors of solutions. We have already begun our consideration of solutions in the previous chapter with our review of the colligative properties. We will now continue that review by examining the nature of solutions, the formation of aqueous solutions, measurements of solution concentration, and finally, the qualitative and quantitative evaluation of solution equilibria.

Nature of Solutions

Many important chemical reactions, both in the laboratory and in nature, take place in solution, including almost all reactions in living organisms. **Solutions** are homogenous (the same throughout) mixtures of two or more substances that combine to form a single phase, usually the liquid phase. The MCAT will focus generally on solids dissolved into liquid aqueous solutions, but it's important to remember that solutions can be formed from different combinations of the three phases of matter. For example, gases can be dissolved in liquids (e.g., the carbonation of soda); liquids can be dissolved in other liquids (e.g., ethanol in water); solids can even be dissolved in other solids (e.g., metal alloys). Incidentally, gases "dissolved" into other gases can be thought of as solutions but are more properly defined as **mixtures,** because gas molecules don't really interact all that much (one of the postulates of the kinetic molecular theory of gases). Just a point of minor clarification: all solutions are considered mixtures, but not all mixtures are considered solutions.

A solution consists of a **solute** (e.g., NaCl, NH_3, $C_6H_{12}O_6$, CO_2, etc.) dissolved (dispersed) in a **solvent** (e.g., H_2O, benzene, ethanol, etc.). The solvent is the component of the solution whose phase remains the same after mixing. If the two substances are already in the same phase, for example, a solution of two liquids, the solvent is the component present in greater quantity. And if the two same-phase components are in equal proportions in the solution, the component considered the solvent is the one that is more commonly identified as a solvent. Solute molecules move about freely in the solvent and interact with the solvent by way of interparticle forces such as ion-dipole, dipole-dipole, or hydrogen bonding. Dissolved solute molecules are also relatively free to interact with other dissolved molecules of different chemical identity; consequently, chemical reactions occur easily in solution.

SOLVATION

Not to be confused with the path to eternal life, **solvation** is the electrostatic interaction between solute and solvent molecules. This is also known as **dissolution,** and when water is the solvent, it is called **hydration** and the resulting solution is an aqueous solution. Solvation involves breaking intermolecular interactions between solute molecules and between solvent molecules and forming new intermolecular interactions between solute and solvent molecules.

When the new interactions (attractions) are stronger than the original ones, solvation is exothermic and the process is favored at low temperatures. The dissolution of gases into liquids, such as CO_2 into water, is an exothermic process because the only significant interactions that must be broken are those between water molecules. CO_2, as a gas, demonstrates minimal intermolecular interaction, and thus the dissolution of CO_2 gas into water is overall exothermic (and Le Châtelier's principle tells us this is the reason that lowering the temperature of a liquid favors solubility of a gas in the liquid.) This is also why opening a two-liter container of warm soda is risky: the warm soda has very low solubility for the CO_2 gas and when the pressure is released upon twisting the cap open, a lot of the CO_2 gas escapes (precipitates, comes out of the solution), with some amount of violence, carrying with it a lot of the liquid itself. We've all seen—or suffered—the aftermath of a warm soda too hastily opened.

When the new interactions (attractions) are weaker than the original ones, solvation is endothermic, and the process is favored at high temperatures. Most dissolutions are of this type. Two such examples have already been given: dissolving sugar or ammonium nitrate into water. Since the new interactions between the solute and solvent are weaker than the original interactions between the solute molecules and between the solvent molecules, energy (heat) must be supplied in order to facilitate the formation of these weaker, less stable interactions. Sometimes the overall strength of the new interactions is approximately equal to the overall strength of the original interactions. In this case, the overall enthalpy change for the dissolution is close to zero. These types of solutions approximate the formation of an **ideal solution,** for which the enthalpy of dissolution is equal to zero.

The spontaneity of dissolution is not only dependent upon the enthalpy change; solutions may form spontaneously for both endothermic and exothermic dissolutions. The second property that contributes to the spontaneity or nonspontaneity of a solution is the entropy change that occurs in the process. At constant temperature and pressure, entropy always increases upon dissolution. As with any process, the spontaneity or nonspontaneity of dissolution depends upon the change in Gibbs function: spontaneous processes result in a decrease of free energy while nonspontaneous processes result in an increase of free energy. Thus whether dissolution will happen spontaneously or not depends upon both the change in enthalpy and change in entropy for the solute and solvent of the system.

Consider, for example, the formation of another common solution, one that we've mentioned a number of times in this book: sodium chloride, table salt, dissolved in water. When NaCl dissolves in water, its component ions dissociate from each other and become surrounded by water molecules. In order for this new interaction to occur, ion-ion interactions between the Na^+ and Cl^- must be broken and hydrogen bonds between water molecules must also be broken. This step requires energy and is therefore endothermic. Because water is polar, it can interact with each of the component ions through ion-dipole interactions: the partially positive hydrogen end of the water molecules will surround the Cl^- ions and the partially negative oxygen end of the water molecules will surround the Na^+ ions. The formation of these ion-dipole bonds is exothermic, but not as great as the endothermicity of breaking the old ones (although it is quite close). As a result, the overall dissolution of table salt into water is endothermic (+0.93 J/mol) and favored at high temperatures.

We've considered the enthalpy change for the formation of a sodium chloride solution, and now we need to examine the entropy change. Remember than entropy can be thought of as the measure of the degree to which energy is disbursed throughout a system or the measure of the amount of energy distributed from the system to the surroundings at a given temperature. Another way to understand entropy is the measure of molecular disorder, or the number of energy microstates available to a system at a given temperature. When solid sodium chloride dissolves into water, the rigidly ordered arrangement of the sodium and chloride ions is broken up, as the ion-ion interactions are disrupted and new ion-dipole interactions with the water molecules are formed. The ions, freed from their lattice arrangement, have a greater number of energy microstates available to them (in simpler terms, they are freer to move around in different ways) and consequently, their energy is more distributed and their entropy increases. The water, however, becomes more restricted in its movement because it is now interacting with the ions. The number of energy microstates available to it (that is, the water molecules' ability to move around in different ways) is reduced and so the entropy of the water decreases. But the increase in the entropy experienced by the dissolved sodium chloride is greater than the decrease in the entropy experienced by the water and so the overall entropy change is positive—energy is overall disbursed by the dissolution of sodium chloride in water. Because of the relatively low endothermicity and relatively large positive change in entropy, sodium chloride will spontaneously dissolve in liquid water.

SOLUBILITY

We need to know more than just whether or not dissolution of a solute into a solvent will be spontaneous or nonspontaneous. We also want to know how much solute will dissolve into a given solvent. The **solubility** of a substance is the maximum amount of that substance that can be dissolved in a particular solvent at a particular temperature. When this maximum amount of solute has been added, the dissolved solute is in equilibrium with its undissolved state, and we say that the solution is **saturated.** If more solute is added, it will not dissolve. For example, at 18°C, a maximum of 83 g of glucose ($C_6H_{12}O_6$) will dissolve in 100 mL of H_2O. Thus the solubility of glucose is 83 g/100 mL. If more glucose is added to an already saturated glucose solution, it will not dissolve, but rather will remain in solid form, **precipitating** to the bottom of the container. A solution in which the proportion of solute to solvent is small is said to be **dilute,** and one in which the proportion is large is said to be **concentrated.** Note that both dilute and concentrated solutions are still considered unsaturated if the maximum equilibrium concentration (saturation) has not been reached.

The solubility of substances into different solvents is ultimately a function of thermodynamics. When the change in Gibbs function is negative at a given temperature for the dissolution of a given solute into a given solvent, the process will be spontaneous and the solute is said to be soluble. When the change in Gibbs function is positive at a given temperature for the dissolution of a given solute into a given solvent, the process will be nonspontaneous and the solute is said to be insoluble. Some solute/solvent systems have very large negative ΔGs, so dissolution is very spontaneous and a lot of solute can be dissolved into the solvent. Others have very small negative ΔGs and so dissolution is only slightly spontaneous and as a result only a little solute can be dissolved into the solvent. Those solutes that dissolve minimally in the solvent (usually water) are called the **sparingly soluble salts.**

AQUEOUS SOLUTIONS

The most common type of solution is the aqueous solution, in which the solvent is water. The aqueous state is denoted by the symbol (*aq*). Because aqueous solutions are so common and so important to biological systems (e.g., you), the MCAT focuses on them above all others. We wish we could tell you otherwise, but for Test Day you are expected to remember the general solubility rules for aqueous solutions. We know, we know—they are not the easiest or most fun to remember, but no one ever promised you that this would always be fun. (We promised you that we would help you have *some* fun in this preparation process.) There are seven general solubility rules:

1. All salts of alkali metals are water soluble.
2. All salts of the ammonium ion (NH_4^+) are water soluble.
3. All chlorides, bromides, and iodides are water soluble, with the exceptions of Ag^+, Pb^{2+}, and Hg_2^{2+}.
4. All salts of the sulfate ion (SO_4^{2-}) are water soluble, with the exceptions of Ca^{2+}, Sr^{2+}, Ba^{2+}, and Pb^{2+}.
5. All metal oxides are insoluble, with the exception of the alkali metals and CaO, SrO, and BaO, all of which hydrolyze to form solutions of the corresponding metal hydroxides.
6. All hydroxides are insoluble, with the exception of the alkali metals and Ca^{2+}, Sr^{2+}, and Ba^{2+}.
7. All carbonates (CO_3^{2-}), phosphates (PO_4^{3-}), sulfides (S^{2-}), and sulfites (SO_3^{2-}) are insoluble, with the exception of the alkali metals and ammonium.

On the MCAT there is one infallible solubility rule: *all sodium salts are completely soluble, and all nitrate salts are completely soluble.* Thus, if a problem gives you a concentration of sodium fluoride, you know that the compound is completely soluble in water. Sodium and nitrate ions are generally used as counterions to what is really chemically important; for example, if a pH problem gives you a sodium formate

MCAT Expertise

Because most solutions involve water as the solvent in the real world, it is not a surprise that they are common on the MCAT. These solubility rules are not bad to know but memorizing it all may be a little excessive. It is never a bad thing to know facts, but being able to apply them is more important. Know rules 1 and 2 for sure and be aware of some of the more common insoluble exceptions, like Pb^{2+} and Ag^+.

concentration of 0.10 M, it is really telling you that the concentration of the formate ion is 0.10 M, because the sodium ion concentration does not affect pH. The only time you need to worry about the nitrate ion concentration is in a redox reaction, for the nitrate ion can function—though only weakly—as an oxidizing agent; otherwise, merely focus on the cation as the chemically reacting species.

Ions

Ionic solutions are of particular interest to chemists because certain important types of chemical reactions—acid-base and oxidation-reduction reactions, for instance—take place in ionic solutions. It shouldn't come as a surprise to you by now that if chemists take particular interest in this area of chemistry, so will the MCAT. In fact, acid-base and oxidation-reduction reactions are themselves important topics for the MCAT and so you can begin your review of those topics (Chapters 10 and 11) by reviewing with us now the characteristics and behaviors of ions.

CATIONS AND ANIONS

Ionic compounds are made up of positively charged cations and negatively charged anions. Ionic compounds are held together by the ionic bond, which is the force of electrostatic attraction between oppositely charged particles. The word "cation" (and especially the organic chemistry variant, "carbocation") has tripped up unsuspecting students for years, who, having never heard the word spoken aloud before, almost invariably pronounce it as the last two syllables of "vacation" (as if a carbocation were some fun carbon-based holiday…we humbly admit to having made the mistake ourselves at a point in the less glorious distant past.)

The nomenclature of ionic compounds is based on the names of the component ions.

1. For elements (usually metals) that can form more than one positive ion, the charge is indicated by a Roman numeral in parentheses following the name of the element.

    Fe^{2+} Iron (II) Cu^+ Copper (I)
    Fe^{3+} Iron (III) Cu^{2+} Copper (II)

2. An older but still commonly used method is to add the endings **-ous** or **-ic** to the root of the Latin name of the element, to represent the ions with lesser or greater charge, respectively.

    Fe^{2+} Ferrous Cu^+ Cuprous
    Fe^{3+} Ferric Cu^{2+} Cupric

Practice Questions

1. An aqueous solution was prepared by mixing 70 grams of a solid into 100 grams of water. The solution has a boiling point of 101.11°C. What is the molar mass of the solute? (K_b = 0.512°C)

   A. 322.58 g/mol
   B. 32.26 g/mol
   C. 123.24 g/mol
   D. 233.59 g/mol

2. Which phase of solvent and solute, respectively, can form a solution?

   I. Solid solvent, gaseous solute
   II. Solid solvent, solid solute
   III. Gaseous solvent, gaseous solute

   A. I and II only
   B. II and III only
   C. I and III only
   D. I, II, and III

3. Two organic liquids, pictured in the figure below, are combined to form a solution. Based on the structures, will the solution closely obey Raoult's law?

   Benzene   Toluene

   A. Yes, the liquids differ due to the additional methyl group on toluene and therefore will not deviate from Raoult's law.
   B. Yes, the liquids are very similar and therefore will not deviate from Raoult's law.
   C. No, the liquids differ due to the additional methyl group on toluene and therefore will deviate from Raoult's law.
   D. No, the liquids both contain benzene rings which will interact with each other and cause deviation from Raoult's law.

4. The diagram in Figure 2 shows two arms separated by an impermeable membrane. What would happen to the level of liquid in the two branches if the membrane was replaced with a semipermeable membrane that allowed water molecules to move across the membrane?

A. The level on the right would decrease and the level on the left would increase.

B. The level would remain the same on both sides.

C. The level on the right would increase and the level on the left would decrease.

D. The level on the right would stay the same and the level on the left would increase.

5. The process of formation of a liquid solution can be better understood by breaking the process into three steps:

1. Breaking the solution into individual components

2. Making room for the solute in the solvent by overcoming intermolecular forces in the solvent

3. Allowing solute-solvent interactions to occur to form the solution

The overall energy change to form a solution can be estimated by taking the sum of each of the three steps. For steps 1 through 3, will each step most likely be endothermic or exothermic? The order for each answer choice is step 1, step 2, followed by step 3.

A. Endothermic, exothermic, endothermic

B. Exothermic, endothermic, endothermic

C. Exothermic, exothermic, endothermic

D. Endothermic, endothermic, exothermic

6. The entropy change when a solution forms can be expressed by the term ΔS°_{soln}. When an ion dissolves and water molecules are ordered around it, the ordering would be expected to make a negative contribution to ΔS°_{soln}. An ion that has more charge density will have a greater hydration effect, or ordering of water molecules. Based on this information, which of the following compounds will have the most negative ΔS°_{soln}?

A. KCl

B. LiF

C. CaS

D. NaCl

7. A 0.01 M solution of a nonelectrolyte has an osmotic pressure of 15.0 mm Hg. What is the osmotic pressure of a 0.02 M solution of $Mg(NO_3)_2$? The temperature of both solutions is the same.

A. 7.5 mm Hg

B. 30 mm Hg

C. 45 mm Hg

D. 90 mm Hg

8. One hundred grams of sugar are dissolved in a cup of hot water at 80°C. The cup of water contains 300.00 mL of water. What is the mass percentage of sugar in the resulting solution? (Sugar = $C_{12}H_{22}O_{11}$, density of water at 80°C = 0.975 g/mL)

A. 25.0%

B. 25.5%

C. 33.3%

D. 34.2%

9. Which of the following combinations of liquids would be expected to have a vapor pressure higher than the vapor pressure that would be predicted by Raoult's law?

A. Ethanol and hexane

B. Acetone and water

C. Isopropanol and methanol

D. Nitric acid and water

10. The salt KCl is dissolved in a beaker of water that you are holding. You can feel the solution cool as the KCl dissolves. From this observation you conclude that

A. ΔS°_{soln} is large enough to overcome the unfavorable ΔH°_{soln}.
B. KCl is mostly insoluble in water.
C. ΔS°_{soln} must be negative when KCl dissolves.
D. Boiling point elevation will occur in this solution.

11. Which of the following will give the greatest increase in the boiling point of water when it is dissolved in 1.00 kg H_2O?

A. 0.46 mol calcium sulfate
B. 0.54 mol iron (III) nitrate
C. 1.09 mol acetic acid
D. 1.11 mol sucrose

12. At sea level and 25°C, the solubility of oxygen gas in water is 1.25×10^{-3} M. In a city in the United States that lies high above sea level, the atmospheric pressure is 0.800 atm. What is the solubility of oxygen in water in this city?

A. 1.05×10^{-3} M
B. 1.56×10^{-3} M
C. 1.00×10^{-3} M
D. 1.25×10^{-3} M

13. Lead is a dangerous element that exists in the environment in large quantities due to man-made pollution. Lead poisoning has many symptoms, including mental retardation in children. If a body of water is polluted with lead ions at 30 ppb (parts per billion), what is the concentration of lead in molarity? (density of water is 1 g/mL, ppb equals grams per 10^9 grams of solution)

A. 6.2×10^{-7} M Pb^{2+}
B. 1.4×10^{-10} M Pb^{2+}
C. 1.4×10^{-7} M Pb^{2+}
D. 6.2×10^{-6} M Pb^{2+}

14. Which of the following is/are correct?

  I. NaF is an electrolyte.
 II. Glucose is a nonelectrolyte.
III. CH_3OH is a weak electrolyte.
 IV. CH_3CH_2COOH is a weak electrolyte.

A. I, III, and IV only
B. I and II only
C. II, and IV only
D. I, II, and IV only

15. Which one of the following is not a colligative property?

A. Boiling point elevation
B. Vapor pressure of a mixture
C. Osmotic pressure
D. Entropy of dissolution

16. The following equilibrium shown in Figure 4 exists when AgBr is in solution:

$$AgBr_{(s)} \longleftrightarrow Ag^+_{(aq)} + Br^-_{(aq)}$$
$$Ksp = 7.7 \times 10^{-13}$$

Calculate the solubility of AgBr in g/L in a solution of 0.0010 M NaBr.

A. 7.7×10^{-13} g/L
B. 8.3×10^{-12} g/L
C. 7.7×10^{-10} g/L
D. 8.3×10^{-8} g/L

17. When ammonia, NH_3, is a solvent, complex ions can form. For example, dissolving AgCl in NH_3 will result in the complex ion $Ag(NH_3)^{2+}$. What effect would you expect the formation of complex ions to have on the solubility of a compound like AgCl in NH_3?

A. The solubility of AgCl will increase because complex ion formation will cause more ions to exist in solution that interact with AgCl to cause it to dissociate.

B. The solubility of AgCl will increase because complex ion formation will consume Ag^+ molecules and cause the equilibrium to shift away from solid AgCl.

C. The solubility of AgCl will decrease because Ag^+ ions are in complexes and the Ag^+ ions that are not complexed will want to associate with Cl^- to form solid AgCl.

D. The solubility of AgCl will decrease because complex ion formation will consume Ag^+ molecules and cause the equilibrium to shift toward the solid AgCl.

18. Detergents are compounds that are dissolved in water. However, they are also able to dissolve hydrophobic stains such as oil and grease in clothing and other fabrics. How are these compounds able to fulfill both hydrophilic and hydrophobic functions?

A. They contain a hydrophobic core molecule encased in a hydrophilic shell.

B. They can ionize into two parts; one part is ionic and the other part is hydrophobic.

C. They have two states; in water they are ionic and in hydrophobic solvents they form nonpolar ring structures.

D. They have two functionally distinct parts; one side is a hydrophobic chain and the other end is polar and ionic.

Small Group Questions

1. How does the presence of common ions in solution affect K_{sp}? I.P. (Q_{sp})?

2. Discuss the circumstances that permit solvation. What forces are involved?

Explanations to Practice Questions

1. A

The equation $\Delta T_b = k_b m_c$ can be used to solve this problem. The change in boiling point is found by subtracting the boiling point of water (the solvent), 100°C, from the elevated boiling point, 101.11°C. Using the given value for k_b, we solve for the molality of the solution and get 2.17 moles/kg. Convert to grams by dividing by 1,000 and then multiply by the mass of the solution, 100 g, to get the moles of solute. To obtain the molar mass, divide the mass of the solute, 70 g, by the number of moles, 0.217 moles, to get a molar mass of 322.58 g/mole. (B) would indicate a problem in unit conversions because the answer is off by an order of magnitude. (C) and (D) are wrong and would result from multiplying 1.11 by the k_b instead of dividing.

2. D

All three choices can make a solution as long as the two components create a mixture that is of uniform appearance (homogenous). Hydrogen in platinum is an example of a gas in a solid. The air we breathe is an example of a homogenous mixture of a gas in a gas. Brass and steel are examples of homogenous mixtures of solids.

3. B

Benzene and toluene are both organic liquids and have very similar properties. They are both nonpolar and are almost exactly the same size. Raoult's law states that ideal solution behavior is observed when solute-solute, solvent-solvent, and solute-solvent interactions are very similar. Therefore, benzene and toluene in solution will be predicted to behave as a nearly ideal solution. (A) states that the liquids would follow Raoult's law because they are different. It is true that the compounds are slightly different but the difference is negligible in terms of Raoult's law. (C) and (D) are incorrect because they state that the solution would not obey Raoult's law.

4. A

If the membrane became permeable to water then water molecules would move to the side with the higher solute concentration, according to the principles of osmosis. The left side has a higher concentration of solute (NaCl), so water will move toward the left in an attempt to balance the concentrations of each side. The level on the left will rise because of the excess water molecules and the level on the right will fall due to a loss of water molecules.

5. D

The first step will most likely be endothermic because energy is required to break molecules apart. The second step is also endothermic because the intermolecular forces in the solvent must be overcome to allow incorporation of solute particles. The third step will most likely be exothermic because polar water molecules will interact with the dissolved ions and release energy.

6. C

CaS will cause the most negative ΔS°_{soln} because the Ca^{2+} and S^{2-} ions have the highest charge density compared to the other ions. All of the other ions have charges of +1 or −1, whereas Ca^{2+} and S^{2-} each have charges with an absolute value of 2. To arrange all four species in order of highest to lowest charge density, we'd have to take ion size into account. Smaller ions have higher charge densities. For example, LiF will have a higher charge density than KCl. It follows that the ΔS°_{soln} is more negative for LiF than for KCl.

7. D

A nonelectrolyte solution will not dissociate into ions in solution. Its effective molarity in solution will be the same as the number of moles that were dissolved. On the other hand, an electrolyte like $Mg(NO_3)_2$ will dissociate into three ions (Mg and $2NO_3^-$). The effective molarity, which is important for colligative properties, will be three times the number of moles that were dissolved. Osmotic pressure is a colligative property and will therefore be three times larger for $Mg(NO_3)_2$ compared to a nonelectrolyte. The molarity of $Mg(NO_3)_2$, 0.02 M, is two times larger than the non-electrolyte solution (0.01 M). The nonelectrolyte's osmotic pressure will have to be multiplied by three and then by two for $Mg(NO_3)_2$. 15 mm Hg × 3 × 2 equals 90 mm Hg. We can use the osmotic pressure formula to check our work.

Osmotic pressure: $\Pi = MRT$

$$T_1 = T_2, \text{ so } \frac{\Pi_1}{M_1 R} = \frac{\Pi_2}{M_2 R}.$$

R terms cancel, and we're solving for Π_2, so we're left with:

$$\Pi_2 = \frac{M_2 \Pi_1}{M_1} = \frac{(0.02 \text{ M})(3 \text{ particles per mol})(15 \text{ mm Hg})}{(0.01 \text{ M})}$$

$$= 90 \text{ mm Hg}$$

8. B

The mass percent of a solute equals the mass of the solute divided by the mass of the total solution. To find the mass of the solution first find the mass of the solvent, water. Multiplying the volume of the solution by the density gives a mass of 292.5 grams of water. Adding 100 grams of sugar yields a solution with a mass of 392.5 grams. Next, divide 100 grams of sugar by 392.5 grams and multiply by 100 to get a percentage. (A) can be arrived at if water's density at 80° is assumed to be 1 g/mL. If we had forgotten to add the solute's mass to the solvent's, we'd have calculated 33.3 percent, which is (C). (D) neglects both the addition step and the correct density value.

9. A

Mixtures that have a higher vapor pressure than predicted by Raoult's law have stronger solvent-solvent and solute-solute interactions than solvent-solute interactions. Therefore, particles do not want to stay in solution and more

readily evaporate, creating a higher vapor pressure than an ideal solution. Two liquids that have different properties, like hexane (hydrophobic) and ethanol (hydrophilic, small) would not have many interactions with each other to cause positive deviation. (B) and (C) are composed of liquids that are similar to one another and that would not show significant deviation from Raoult's law because they neither attract nor repel one another. (D) contains two liquids that would interact well with each other, causing a negative deviation from Raoult's law. When attracted to one other, liquids prefer to stay in liquid form and have a lower vapor pressure than predicted by Raoult's law.

10. A

Dissolution is governed by enthalpy and entropy, which are related by the equation $\Delta G°_{soln} = \Delta H°_{soln} - T\Delta S°_{soln}$. The cooling of the solution indicates that heat is used up in this bond-breaking reaction. In other words, dissolution is endothermic and ΔH is positive. The reaction is occurring spontaneously, so ΔG must be negative. The only way that a positive ΔH can result in a negative ΔG is if entropy, ΔS, is a large, positive value. If $T\Delta S$ has a larger absolute value than ΔH, ΔG will be negative. Conceptually, that means that the only way the solid can dissolve is if the increase in entropy is great enough to overcome the decrease in enthalpy. (B) is incorrect because it is clearly stated in the question stem that KCl dissolves. (C) is incorrect because $\Delta S°_{soln}$ must be positive in order for KCl to dissolve. Finally, (D) is incorrect because solute dissolution would cause boiling point to elevate, not depress. Additionally, it is not a piece of evidence that could be found simply by observing the beaker's temperature change.

11. D

The equation to determine the change in boiling point of a solution is as follows: $\Delta T_b = m_b(K_b)$. m_b is the molality of the solution and K_b is the boiling point elevation constant. In this case, the solvent is always water, so K_b will be the same for each solution and we don't need it to find our answer. What we do need to know is how many particles dissociate from each original species. This is referred to as the van't Hoff factor (i) and is multiplied by our molality to demonstrate an effective molality. We'll use effective molality values to determine which will cause the greatest change in boiling point.

Species	Number of Moles	Number of Dissolved Particles	$i \times m$ (Effective Molality)
$CaSO_4$	0.46	2	0.92
$Fe(NO_3)_3$	0.54	4	2.16
CH_3COOH	1.09	Some 2, most 1	1.09 < x < 2.18
$C_{12}H_{22}O_{11}$	1.11	1	1.11

It looks like we need to decide between iron (III) nitrate and acetic acid. No more calculations are necessary because the fact that acetic acid is a weak acid tells us that only a few particles will dissociate into H^+ and acetate$^-$. So the "x" that we are curious about is most likely closer to 1.09 than 2.18. We can certainly conclude that it will be less than 2.16. Iron (III) nitrate will have the largest effect on boiling point.

12. C

The solubility of gases in liquids is directly proportional to the atmospheric pressure. Therefore, we should expect a decrease in solubility upon experiencing the decreased atmospheric pressure in Denver. 0.800 atm is 80% of the pressure at sea level (1 atm), so oxygen's solubility will be 80% of 1.25×10^{-3}, which yields 1.00×10^{-3} M. (A) is a miscalculation, (B) suggests that pressure and solubility are inversely related, and (D) implies that atmospheric temperature will not affect solubility.

13. C

30 ppb of Pb^{2+} is equivalent to 30 grams of Pb^{2+} in 10^9 grams of solution. Water's density will help us convert from mass to volume. Dividing by the molar mass of Pb^{2+}, 207 g/mole, will result in Pb^{2+}'s molarity, 1.4×10^{-7} M.

$$\frac{(30 \text{ g Pb}^{2+})(1 \text{ g H}_2\text{O})(1{,}000 \text{ mL})(1 \text{ mol Pb}^{2+})}{(10^9 \text{ g H}_2\text{O})(1 \text{ mL H}_2\text{O})(1 \text{ L})(207 \text{ g Pb}^{2+})} = 1.44 \times 10^{-7} \text{ M}$$

14. D

An electrolyte is a molecule that dissociates into free ions and behaves as an electrically conductive medium. Number I, NaF, is an electrolyte because it dissociates to form the ions Na^+ and F^-. Number II, glucose, is a nonelectrolyte because it has a ring structure that dissolves but does not dissociate. Number III, CH_3OH, has a pKa of approximately 15, and is not likely to ionize in solution. Therefore, it is not an electrolyte. Number IV, acetic acid, is a weak acid (pKa = 4.7) and also a weak electrolyte because it will partially ionize in solution.

15. D

A colligative property depends solely upon the number of molecules and disregards the identity of the molecules. (A), (B), and (C) are all properties based on the composition of a solution, determined by the number of molecules that are dissolved in the solution. (D), the entropy of dissolution, will depend on the chemical properties of the substance, such as charge density and electron affinity. Therefore, the entropy of dissolution is not a colligative property.

16. D

The solubility of AgBr can be solved by using the K_{sp} value given in the equation.

$$AgBr \leftrightarrow Ag^+ + Br^-$$
$$K_{sp} = [Ag^+][Br^-] = 7.7 \times 10^{-13}$$

Assuming that the same amount of cations and anions dissolve, we can refer to Ag^+ and Br^- both as "x."

$$K_{sp} = [x][x] = 7.7 \times 10^{-13}$$

However, there is already 0.001 M Br^- in solution. To account for that, we'll add it in to the K_{sp} equation.

$$K_{sp} = [x][x + 0.001 \text{ M}] = 7.7 \times 10^{-13}$$

We know 0.001 is much bigger than the square root of 10^{-13}. In other words, it's much bigger than x, and x is insignificant in comparison. So we'll approximate Br^-'s concentration as 0.001 M and solve for silver. The solubility of Ag^+ is the same as AgBr's because one molecule of Ag^+ dissociates per molecule of AgBr.

$$K_{sp} = [x][\cancel{x} + 0.001 \text{ M}] = 7.7 \times 10^{-13}$$
$$K_{sp} = [x][0.001 \text{ M}] = 7.7 \times 10^{-13}$$
$$x = \frac{7.7 \times 10^{-13}}{1 \times 10^{-3}} = 7.7 \times 10^{-10} \text{ M}$$

We find that $[Ag^+]$ is 7.7×10^{-10} M Ag^+. This value can be converted to g/L by multiplying by the molar mass of silver, 107.9 grams/mole.

$$(7.7 \times 10^{-10} \text{ mol/L})(107.9 \text{ g/mol}) = 8.3 \times 10^{-8} \text{ g/L}$$

17. B

Formation of complex ions between silver ions and ammonia will cause more molecules of solid AgCl to dissociate. The equilibrium is driven toward dissociation because the Ag^+ ions are essentially being removed from solution when they complex with ammonia. This rationale is based upon Le Châtelier's principle, stating that when a chemical equilibrium experiences a change in concentration, the system will shift to counteract that change. (A) is incorrect because the complex ions may interact with AgCl but this is not the major reason for the increased solubility. (C) and (D) are incorrect because the solubility of AgCl will increase, not decrease.

18. D

Detergents are compounds that contain a long hydrophobic chain with a polar functional group on one end. The long hydrophobic chains can surround grease and oil droplets, while the polar heads face outward and carry the particles in a solution of water. (A) describes micelles, which are very different in configuration. (B) is internally inconsistent because ionization creates two ionic particles. (C) is incorrect because although multiple detergent molecules form a sphere-like shape with oil or grease droplets enclosed, the individual molecules themselves do not form ring structures.

Acids and Bases

There are many ways that drugs can enter the human body. The route of administration of a drug is the path by which that drug comes into contact with the body. According to the U.S. Food and Drug Administration's Data Standards Manual, there are no fewer than 110 distinct ways in which a drug can come in contact with and/or enter the human body in a local or systemic manner, including the catch-all route of "other." Some drugs can be applied as drops, salves, or creams to mucus membranes. Others are injected. Some employ a transdermal patch, while others are eaten, drunk, or inhaled. You will be challenged in medical school to learn and recall the routes of administration for many commonly prescribed medications and treatments. This is one of the more daunting memorization tasks that will be demanded of you during medical school and residency.

The route of administration of a drug compound is related to both the location of its target tissue (local or systemic) as well as the chemical and physical properties of the compound. For example, compounds that are water-soluble can be administered intravenously (an aqueous solution dripped directly into the bloodstream), while those that are lipid-soluble can be administered transcutaneously (from, say, a patch or a cream) or orally (in a pill or liquid suspension). The polarity, size, and charge of the drug compound will determine its solubility in polar or nonpolar environments and will be major contributing factors to the most effective and efficient route of administration.

Whether a drug compound has an ionic charge is usually a function of the acidic or basic nature of the compound. For example, a basic organic compound that is water-insoluble when neutral can be reacted with an acid to form a salt that, because it is ionic, will be water-soluble. Correspondingly, an acidic organic compound that is water-insoluble when neutral can be reacted with a base to form a water-soluble salt. On the other hand, the protonated (acidic) form of an organic compound can be reacted with a base to neutralize the compound and release it from its salt, changing (and usually reversing) its solubility in water.

Medical professionals aren't the only ones concerned about drug solubilities and routes of administration. There's a science to illegal drugs, too. People in the general population who use illegal drugs (and those who produce them) are knowledgeable about their available forms as well as the most effective and efficient modes of delivery. One of the clearest examples of this is the difference in the ways that people use the two forms of cocaine. $C_{17}H_{21}NO_4$ (cocaine) is a large alkaloid compound derived from the coca plant. It is a central nervous stimulant that has been used medicinally, ceremonially, and recreationally since at least the Pre-Columbian era. About 125 years ago, Pope Leo XIII purportedly carried around a hipflask filled with cocaine-laced wine called Vin Mariani. The 1886 original recipe for what is now the world's most famous cola included coca leaves (from which this famous cola derives its name). Cocaine was once used to treat heroin addiction. Sigmund Freud wrote rhapsodically about its ability to cause "exhilaration and lasting euphoria." By 1903, however, the *American Journal of Pharmacy* was warning that most cocaine abusers were "bohemians, gamblers, high- and low-class prostitutes, night porters, bell boys, burglars, racketeers, pimps, and casual laborers."

Today, cocaine is used primarily in two different forms. Most commonly, the alkaloid compound is reacted with hydrochloric acid (which protonates its tertiary amine functional group), extracted with water, and dried to an aqueous soluble powder (cocaine hydrochloride) that either is snorted (insufflated) into the nasal cavity where it is absorbed into the capillary beds or is injected directly into the venous circulation. The salt form, however, because it has a very high boiling point close to the temperature at which it burns, cannot be smoked. To produce a form of cocaine that can be vaporized and inhaled from a pipe, the cocaine hydrochloride must be reacted with a base, typically either ammonia (to produce pure "freebase cocaine") or sodium bicarbonate (to produce the less-pure "crack" cocaine). The base reacts with the protonated tertiary amine, removing the hydrogen ion to re-form the neutral alkaloid compound. The freebase cocaine is water-insoluble and usually extracted with ether, or left in the aqueous solution, which is heated and evaporated. The freebase or crack form of cocaine has a much lower boiling point; consequently, it can be smoked without risk of burning (combusting).

What a difference a little hydrogen ion can make! The complexities of drug delivery can in part be related to the presence or absence of the hydrogen ion—a mere proton! In this chapter, our focus will be those two classes of compounds—acids and bases—that are involved in so many important reactions. Acid-base reactions are an important focus for the MCAT; in fact, the neutralization reaction is one of the most commonly tested reaction types on Test Day. We will begin with a review of the different definitions of acids and bases and their properties, including the characterization of acids and bases as either strong or weak. Focusing on weak acids and bases, we will discuss the significance of the equilibrium constants, K_a and K_b, for acids and bases, respectively. Finally, we will review acid-base titrations and buffer systems.

Definitions

Over the last century, chemists have used different definitions to identify compounds as acids or bases. Three definitions have been proposed and each is progressively more inclusive: every Arrhenius acid (or base) can also be classified as a Brønsted-Lowry acid (or base), and every Brønsted-Lowry acid (or base) can also be classified as a Lewis acid (or base).

The pH of a solution is given by:

$$pH = -\log[H^+] = \log(1/[H^+])$$

Likewise, the pOH of a solution is given by:

$$pOH = -\log[OH^-] = \log(1/[OH^-])$$

For pure water at equilibrium at 298 K, the concentration of the hydrogen ion equals the concentration of the hydroxide ion and is 10^{-7} mol/L. Therefore, pure water at 298 K has a pH of 7 and a pOH of 7. (Note: $-\log 10^{-7} = 7$.)

From the water dissociation constant expression ($K_w = [H_3O^+][OH^-] = 10^{-14}$), we find that:

$$pH + pOH = 14 \quad \text{(for aqueous solutions at 298 K)}$$

For any aqueous solution at 298 K, a pH less than 7 (or pOH greater than 7) indicates a relative excess of hydrogen ions, and the solution is acidic; a pH greater than 7 (or pOH less than 7) indicates a relative excess of hydroxide ions, and the solution is basic. A pH (or pOH) equal to 7 indicates equal concentrations of hydrogen and hydroxide ions, resulting in a neutral solution.

Estimating p-Scale Values

An essential skill that you must hone for Test Day, applicable to many problems involving acids and bases, is the ability to quickly convert pH, pOH, pK_a, and pK_b values into nonlogarithmic form and vice versa.

When the original value is a power of 10, the operation is relatively straightforward: changing the sign on the exponent gives the corresponding p-scale value directly. For example:

If $[H+] = 0.001$ or 10^{-3}, then the pH = 3 and pOH = 11
If $K_b = 1.0 \times 10^{-7}$, then $pK_b = 7$

More difficulty arises (in the absence of a calculator or a superhuman ability to calculate logarithms in your head) when the original value is not an exact power of 10. The MCAT is not a math test, and it is not primarily interested in determining your ability to perform mathematical calculations. Exact calculation of the logarithmic value of a number that is not an integer power of 10 will be excessively onerous, if not outright impossible. The test writers are interested, however, in testing your ability to apply mathematical concepts appropriately in solving certain problems. Fortunately, there is a simple method of approximation that will be foolproof for Test Day.

Key Concept

This equation demonstrates a fundamental property of logarithms: the log of a product is equal to the sum of the logs, i.e., $\log(xy) = \log x + \log y$.

MCAT Expertise

Other important properties of logarithms include:

$\log x^n = n \log x$ and $\log 10^x = x$. From these two properties, one can derive the particularly useful relationship that will be seen on Test Day (and we can see in the example): $-\log 10^{-x} = x$.

If the nonlogarithmic value is written in proper scientific notation, it will look like: $n \times 10^{-m}$, where n is a number between 1 and 10. Using the basic log rule that the $\log(xy) = \log x + \log y$, we can express the negative log of this product, $-\log(n \times 10^{-m})$, as $-\log(n) - \log(10^{-m})$. Since log refers to the common log with base of 10, we can simplify $-\log(n) - \log(10^{-m})$ to $-\log(n) - (-m)$, or $m - \log(n)$. Now, since n is a number between 1 and 10, its logarithm will be a fraction between 0 and 1 (note: $\log 1 = 0$ and $\log 10 = 1$). Thus, $m - \log(n)$ will be between $(m - 1)$ and $(m - 0)$. Furthermore, the larger n is (that is, the closer to 10), the larger the fraction, $\log(n)$ will be; consequently, the closer to $(m - 1)$ our answer will be. If this is too much to remember, and, given the amount of information you need to remember for Test Day, it might be, all you need to remember is this: when the nonlogarithmic value is $n \times 10^{-m}$, the logarithmic value will be between $(m - 1)$ and m. It's that simple!

> **Example:** If $K_a = 1.8 \times 10^{-5}$, then $pK_a = 5 - \log 1.8$. Because 1.8 is small, its log will be small, and the answer will be closer to 5 than to 4. (The actual answer is 4.74.)

STRONG ACIDS AND BASES

Strong acids and bases are those that completely dissociate (or nearly so) into their component ions in aqueous solution. For example, when sodium hydroxide, NaOH, is added to water, the ionic compound dissociates, for all intents and purposes, completely according to the net ionic equation:

$$NaOH\ (s) = Na^+\ (aq) + OH^-\ (aq)$$

Hence, in a 1 M solution of NaOH, complete dissociation gives 1 M OH^-. The pH and pOH for this solution can be calculated as:

$$pH = 14 - pOH = 14 - (-\log[OH^-]) = 14 + \log(1) = 14 + 0 = 14$$

Virtually no undissociated strong acid or base, such as NaOH, remains in solution, and we can consider the dissociation of strong acids and bases essentially as going to completion. In the NaOH example given above, you should note that in calculating the pH, we assumed that the concentration of OH^- associated with the auto-ionization of water is negligible compared to the concentration of OH^- due to the addition of the strong base. The contribution of OH^- and H^+ ions to an aqueous solution from the auto-ionization of water can be neglected only if the concentration of the acid or base is significantly greater than 10^{-7} M. Keeping this in mind as you solve acid-base problems on Test Day will help you avoid "silly" mistakes. For example, with your brain on "autopilot" you might calculate the pH of a 1×10^{-8} M solution of HCl (a strong acid) as 8, because $-\log(10^{-8}) = 8$. But a pH of 8 can't possibly describe an acidic solution (at least not at 298 K) because the presence of the acid will cause the hydrogen ion concentration to increase above 10^{-7} and the pH must be below 7.

So what went wrong in this case? The error was in not recognizing that the acid compound concentration is actually ten times less than the equilibrium concentration of hydrogen ions in pure water generated by water's autodissociation. Consequently, the hydrogen ion concentration from the water itself is significant and can't be ignored. Now, the addition of the acid results in the common ion effect (Le Châtelier's principle in action in ionic solutions) and causes the water system to shift away from the side of the ions, thereby reducing the concentration of hydrogen ions and hydroxide ions. The reversal of auto-ionization is thermodynamically favored to return the water system to equilibrium and we can express this mathematically as:

$$K_w = [H_3O^+][OH^-] = [x + (1.0 \times 10^{-8})](x) = 10^{-14}$$

where $x = [H_3O^+] = [OH^-]$ from the auto-ionization of water. Solving for x (using a calculator!) gives $x = 9.5 \times 10^{-8}$ M. The total concentration of hydrogen ions, $[H^+]_{total} = 9.5 \times 10^{-8} + 1.0 \times 10^{-8} = 1.05 \times 10^{-7}$ M. Notice that this indeed is slightly less than what the value would be if the common ion effect were not acting here $[(1.0 \times 10^{-7}) + (1.0 \times 10^{-8}) = 1.1 \times 10^{-7}]$. The pH of this acid solution can now be calculated as pH $= -\log (1.05 \times 10^{-7}) = 6.98$. This value is slightly less than 7, as it should be expected for a very dilute acidic solution. The point of all of this is: *don't put your brain on autopilot on Test Day. Be alert and keep thinking critically, no matter how familiar the problem setups might seem to you!*

Strong acids commonly encountered in the laboratory and on the MCAT include HCl (hydrochloric acid), HBr (hydrobromic acid), HI (hydroiodic acid), H_2SO_4 (sulfuric acid), HNO_3 (nitric acid), and $HClO_4$ (perchloric acid). Strong bases commonly encountered include NaOH (sodium hydroxide), KOH (potassium hydroxide), and other soluble hydroxides of group IA and IIA metals. Calculation of the pH and pOH of strong acids and bases assumes complete dissociation of the acid or base in solution: $[H^+]$ = normality of strong acid and $[OH^-]$ = normality of strong base.

WEAK ACIDS AND BASES

Before we go any further in our discussion of acids and bases as "strong" or "weak," we want to ensure that you are making the mental distinction between the chemical behavior of an acid or base with respect to its tendency to dissociate (e.g., strong bases completely dissociate in aqueous solutions) and the concentration of acid and base solutions. Although we may casually describe a solution's concentration as "strong" or "weak," it is preferable to use the terms "concentrated" and "dilute," respectively, because they are unambiguously associated with concentrations, not chemical behavior.

MCAT Expertise

Always be sure to think about the answer and whether it makes sense on Test Day. As seen in this paragraph, a basic pH for an acidic solution should make you think about what might be wrong with your answer.

MCAT Expertise

The K_w (like all equilibrium constants) will change if the temperature changes and, in turn, will change the pH scale. So be careful on the MCAT because our pH scale of 1–14 is only valid at 25°C.

Continuing our focus on the chemical behavior of acids and bases, we now must consider those acids and bases that only partially dissociate in aqueous solutions. These are called weak acids and bases. For example, a weak monoprotic acid, HA, will dissociate partially in water to achieve an equilibrium state:

$$HA\ (aq) + H_2O\ (l) \leftrightarrow H_3O^+\ (aq) + A^-\ (aq)$$

Since the system exists in an equilibrium state, we can write the dissociation equation to determine the **acid dissociation constant K_a** as:

$$K_a = \frac{[H_3O^+][A^-]}{[HA]}$$

The smaller the K_a, the weaker the acid, and consequently, the less it will dissociate. Note that the concentration of water, while not seemingly included in the dissociation constant expression, is actually incorporated into the value of K_a: ($K_{eq}\ [H_2O] = K_a$).

A weak monovalent base, BOH, undergoes dissociation to yield B^+ and OH^- in solution:

$$BOH\ (aq) \leftrightarrow B^+\ (aq) + OH^-\ (aq)$$

And the **base dissociation constant K_b** can be calculated according to:

$$K_b = \frac{[B^+][OH^-]}{[BOH]}$$

The smaller the K_b, the weaker the base, and consequently, the less it will dissociate. As with the acid dissociation expression, the base dissociation expression incorporates the concentration of the water in the value of the K_b itself.

Generally speaking, we can characterize a species as a weak acid if its K_a is less than 1.0 and as a weak base if its K_b is less than 1.0. On the MCAT, molecular (that is, nonionic) weak bases are almost exclusively amines.

CONJUGATE ACID/BASE PAIRS

Since Brønsted and Lowry define an acid-base reaction as one in which a hydrogen ion (proton) is transferred from the acid to the base, the acid and base always occur in pairs called conjugates. A **conjugate acid** is the acid formed when a base gains a proton and a **conjugate base** is the base that is formed when an acid loses a proton. For example:

$$HCO_3^-\ (aq) + H_2O \leftrightarrow CO_3^{2-}\ (aq) + H_3O^+\ (aq)$$

The CO_3^{2-} is the conjugate base of the HCO_3^- acid and the H_3O^+ is the conjugate acid of the H_2O base. To find the K_a, we consider the equilibrium concentrations of the dissolved species:

$$K_a = \frac{[CO_3^{2-}][H_3O^+]}{[HCO_3^-]}$$

The reaction between bicarbonate (HCO_3^-) and water is reversible, so we can write it as:

$$CO_3^{2-}\,(aq) + H_2O\,(aq) \leftrightarrow HCO_3^-\,(aq) + OH^-\,(aq)$$

and the K_b for CO_3^{2-} as:

$$K_b = \frac{[HCO_3^-][OH^-]}{[CO_3^{2-}]}$$

In a conjugate acid-base pair formed from a weak acid, the conjugate base is generally stronger than the conjugate acid. Note that this does not necessarily mean that a weak acid will produce a strong conjugate base or that a weak base will produce a strong conjugate acid, although it is always the case that a strong acid will produce a weak conjugate base (e.g., HCl/Cl^-) and a strong base will produce a weak conjugate acid (e.g., $NaOH/H_2O$). As it turns out, for HCO_3^- and CO_3^{2-}, the reaction of CO_3^{2-} with water to produce HCO_3^- and OH^- occurs to a greater extent (that is, is thermodynamically more favorable) than the reaction of HCO_3^- and water to produce CO_3^{2-} and H_3O^+.

When you add the previous two reversible reactions, you see that the net is simply the dissociation of water:

$$H_2O\,(l) + H_2O\,(l) \leftrightarrow H_3O^+\,(aq) + OH^-\,(aq)$$

Since the net reaction is the auto-ionization of water, the equilibrium constant for the reaction is $K_w = [H_3O^+][OH^-] = 10^{-14}$, which is the product of K_a and K_b. Remember: the product of the concentrations of the hydrogen ion and the hydroxide ion must always equal 10^{-14} for acid or base aqueous solutions. Because water itself is an amphoteric species (both a weak acid and a weak base), all acid-base reactivity in water ultimately reduces to the acid-base behavior of water, and all acid or base aqueous solutions are governed by the dissociation constant for water. Thus, if the dissociation constant for either the acid or its conjugate base is known, then the dissociation constant for the other can be determined using the equation:

$$K_a \text{ (conjugate acid)} \times K_b \text{(conjugate base)} = K_w = 10^{-14}$$

As you can now see, K_a and K_b are inversely related. In other words, if K_a is large, then K_b is small, and vice versa.

APPLICATIONS OF K_a AND K_b

The most common use of the acid and base dissociation constants is for the determination of the concentration of one of the species in the solution at equilibrium. On Test Day, you may be challenged to calculate the concentration of the hydrogen ion (or pH), the concentration of the hydroxide ion (or pOH), or the concentration of either the original acid or base. One such example is provided below to show you the important steps in solving quickly and correctly these types of problems.

To calculate the concentration of H^+ in a 2.0 M aqueous solution of acetic acid, CH_3COOH ($K_a = 1.8 \times 10^{-5}$), first write the equilibrium reaction:

$$CH_3COOH\ (aq) \leftrightarrow H^+\ (aq) + CH_3COO^-\ (aq)$$

Next, write the expression for the acid dissociation constant:

$$K_a = \frac{[H+][CH_3COO^-]}{[CH_3COOH]} = 1.8 \times 10^{-5}$$

Acetic acid is a weak acid, so the concentration of CH_3COOH at equilibrium is equal to its initial concentration, 2.0 M, less the amount dissociated, x. Likewise $[H^+] = [CH_3COO^-] = x$, because each molecule of CH_3COOH dissociates into one H^+ ion and one CH_3COO^- ion. Thus, the equation can be rewritten as follows:

$$K_a = \frac{[x][x]}{[2.0 - x]} = 1.8 \times 10^{-5}$$

We can approximate that $2.0 - x \approx 2.0$ because acetic acid is a weak acid, and only slightly dissociates in water. This simplifies the calculation of x:

$$K_a = \frac{[x][x]}{[2.0]} = 1.8 \times 10^{-5}$$
$$x = 6.0 \times 10^{-3}\ M$$

The fact that $[x]$ is so much less than the initial concentration of acetic acid (2.0 M) validates the approximation; otherwise, it would have been necessary to solve for x using the quadratic formula. That sounds rather unpleasant, doesn't it? Fortunately for you, the MCAT test writers select examples of weak acids and bases that allow you to make this approximation. (A rule of thumb is that the approximation is valid as long as x is less than 5 percent of the initial concentration.)

Key Concept

Once again, we are dealing with an equilibrium process here and can apply those principles to the problems dealing with weak acids and bases on the exam.

MCAT Expertise

This estimation makes life easy and will get you the correct answer on Test Day.

Salt Formation

Acids and bases may react with each other, forming a salt (and often, but not always, water), in what is termed a **neutralization reaction** (see Chapter 4, Compounds and Stoichiometry). For example,

$$HA + BOH \leftrightarrow BA + H_2O$$

The salt may precipitate out or remain ionized in solution, depending on its solubility and the amount produced. Neutralization reactions generally go to completion. The reverse reaction, in which the salt ions react with water to give back the acid or base, is known as **hydrolysis.**

Four combinations of strong and weak acids and bases are possible:

1. Strong acid + strong base: e.g., $HCl + NaOH \leftrightarrow NaCl + H_2O$
2. Strong acid + weak base: e.g., $HCl + NH_3 \leftrightarrow NH_4Cl$
3. Weak acid + strong base: e.g., $HClO + NaOH \leftrightarrow NaClO + H_2O$
4. Weak acid + weak base: e.g., $HClO + NH_3 \leftrightarrow NH_4ClO$

The products of a reaction between equal concentrations of a strong acid and a strong base are a salt and water. The acid and base neutralize each other, so the resulting solution is neutral (pH = 7), and the ions formed in the reaction do not react with water.

The product of a reaction between a strong acid and a weak base is also a salt, but often no water is formed because weak bases are usually not hydroxides. However, in this case, the cation of the salt will react with the water solvent, reforming the weak base. This reaction constitutes **hydrolysis.** For example:

$$HCl\ (aq) + NH_3\ (aq) \leftrightarrow NH_4^+\ (aq) + Cl^-\ (aq)\ \ \text{Reaction I}$$
$$NH_4^+\ (aq) + H_2O\ (l) \leftrightarrow NH_3\ (aq) + H_3O^+\ (aq)\ \ \text{Reaction II}$$

NH_4^+ is the conjugate acid of a weak base (NH_3), which is stronger than the conjugate base (Cl^-) of the strong acid HCl. NH_4^+ will then transfer a proton to H_2O to form the hydronium ion. The increase in the concentration of the hydronium ion will cause the water system to shift away from auto-ionization, thereby reducing the concentration of hydroxide ion. Consequently, the concentration of the hydrogen ion will be greater than that of the hydroxide ion at equilibrium and, as a result, the pH of the solution will fall below 7.

On the other hand, when a weak acid reacts with a strong base, the pH of the solution at equilibrium is in the basic range because the salt hydrolyzes to re-form the acid,

Bridge

Remember the reaction types discussed in Chapter 4? Well, here is our neutralization reaction.

with the concurrent formation of hydroxide ion from the hydrolyzed water molecules. The increase in the concentration of the hydroxide ion will cause the water system to shift away from auto-ionization, thereby reducing the concentration of the hydrogen ion. Consequently, the concentration of the hydroxide ion will be greater than that of the hydrogen ion at equilibrium and, as a result, the pH of the solution will rise above 7. Consider the reaction of acetic acid CH_3COOH (weak acid) with sodium hydroxide NaOH (strong base):

$$CH_3COOH\ (aq) + NaOH\ (aq) \leftrightarrow Na^+\ (aq) + CH_3COO^-\ (aq) + H_2O\ (l)\ \text{Reaction I}$$
$$CH_3COO^-\ (aq) + H_2O\ (l) \leftrightarrow CH_3COOH\ (aq) + OH^-\ (aq)\ \text{Reaction II}$$

The pH of a solution containing a weak acid and a weak base depends on the relative strengths of the reactants. For example, the acid HClO has a $K_a = 3.2 \times 10^{-8}$, and the base NH_3 has a $K_b = 1.8 \times 10^{-5}$. Thus, an aqueous solution of HClO and NH_3 is basic because the K_a for HClO is less than the K_b for NH_3 (that is to say, HClO is weaker as an acid than NH_3 is as a base, and consequently, at equilibrium, the concentration of hydroxide ions will be greater than the concentration of hydrogen ions in the aqueous solution).

Polyvalence and Normality

The relative acidity or basicity of an aqueous solution is determined by the relative concentrations of **acid** and **base equivalents.** An acid equivalent is equal to one mole of H^+ (or H_3O^+) ions; a base equivalent is equal to one mole of OH^- ions. Some acids and bases are **polyvalent,** that is, each mole of the acid or base liberates more than one acid or base equivalent. For example, the divalent acid H_2SO_4 undergoes the following dissociation in water:

$$H_2SO_4(aq) + H_2O\ (l) \leftrightarrow H_3O^+\ (aq) + HSO_4^-\ (aq)$$
$$HSO_4^-(aq) + H_2O\ (l) \leftrightarrow H_3O^+\ (aq) + SO_4^{2-}(aq)$$

One mole of H_2SO_4 can produce two acid equivalents (2 moles of H_3O^+). You'll notice, if you look closely at the dissociation reaction for sulfuric acid, the first dissociation goes to completion but the second dissociation goes to an equilibrium state. The acidity or basicity of a solution depends upon the concentration of acidic or basic equivalents that can be liberated. The quantity of acidic or basic capacity is directly indicated by the solution's normality (see Chapter 9, Solutions). For example, since each mole of H_3PO_4 can yield three moles (equivalents) of H_3O^+, a 2 M H_3PO_4 solution would be 6 N (6 normal).

Another measurement useful for acid-base chemistry is **equivalent weight.** Chapter 4 defined and discussed this extensively, and Chapter 9 reviewed it briefly. The gram equivalent weight is the mass of a compound that produces one equivalent (one mole of charge). For example, H_2SO_4 (molar mass: 98 g/mol) is a divalent acid, so each mole of the acid compound yields two acid equivalents. The gram equivalent weight is 98/2 = 49 grams. That is, the complete dissociation of 49 grams of H_2SO_4 will yield one acid equivalent (one mole of H_3O^+). Common polyvalent acids include H_2SO_4, H_3PO_4, and H_2CO_3. Common polyvalent bases include $CaCO_3$, $Ca(OH)_2$, and $Mg(OH)_2$. Magnesium hydroxide is the active ingredient in the thick "milky" over-the-counter preparation that is used as an antidote for occasional acid indigestion and diarrhea. Calcium carbonate ($CaCO_3$) is the active ingredient in the over-the-counter tablet preparation also used to treat an upset tummy.

Amphoteric Species

An **amphoteric,** or **amphiprotic,** species is one that reacts like an acid in a basic environment and like a base in an acidic environment. In the Brønsted-Lowry sense, an amphoteric species can either gain or lose a proton. Water is the most common example. When water reacts with a base, it behaves as an acid:

$$H_2O + B^- \leftrightarrow HB + OH^-$$

When water reacts with an acid, it behaves as a base:

$$HA + H_2O \leftrightarrow H_3O^+ + A^-$$

The partially dissociated conjugate base of a polyvalent acid is usually amphoteric (e.g., HSO_4^- can either gain an H^+ to form H_2SO_4, or lose an H^+ to form SO_4^{2-}). The hydroxides of certain metals, e.g., Al, Zn, Pb, and Cr, are also amphoteric. Furthermore, species that can act as either oxidizing or reducing agents (see Chapter 11, Redox Reactions and Electrochemistry) are considered to be amphoteric as well, because by accepting or donating electron pairs they act as Lewis acids or bases, respectively. A simple way of remembering the meaning of the term is to think of amphibian animals, such as frogs. Amphibians live both on land and in water; water is the most common amphoteric species, being able to act as both an acid and a base: *amph*ibians (both land and water living) = *amph*oteric compounds (both acid and base). As you might suspect, this is no mere linguistic coincidence; "amphi" comes from the Greek prefix meaning *on both sides* or *of both kinds*.

Bridge

Recall that we spoke about gram equivalent weights in Chapter 4 and about normality and all units of concentration in Chapter 9.

Titration and Buffers ★★★★☆

Titration is a procedure used to determine the molarity of a known reactant in a solution. There are different types of titrations, including redox, acid-base, and complexometric (metal ion). The MCAT will likely test your understanding of titration procedures and calculations in the context of acid-base solutions. (Metal ion titration may appear on Test Day, but it is less commonly tested and will likely have an informative passage attached.) Titration is a common laboratory procedure and almost certainly you have performed at least one titration (probably acid-base) in your academic career.

Titrations are accomplished by reacting a known volume of a solution of unknown concentration (called the titrand) with a known volume of a solution of known concentration (called the titrant). In acid-base titration, the **equivalence point** is reached when the number of acid equivalents present in the original solution equals the number of base equivalents added, or vice versa. It is important to emphasize that, while a strong acid/strong base titration will have an equivalence point at pH 7, the equivalence point *need not* always occur at pH 7. Also, when titrating polyprotic acids or bases (discussed later in this chapter), there are several equivalence points, as each different acidic or basic conjugate species is titrated separately. In problems involving titration or neutralization of acids and bases, the equation to remember is:

$$N_a V_a = N_b V_b \, ,$$

where N_a and N_b are the acid and base normalities, respectively, and V_a and V_b are the volumes of acid and base solutions, respectively. (Note that as long as both volumes use the same units, the units used do not have to be liters.)

The equivalence point in an acid-base titration is determined in two common ways: either evaluated by using a graphical method, plotting the pH of the titrand solution as a function of added titrant by using a **pH meter** (see Figure 10.1), or estimated by watching for a color change of an added **indicator.** Indicators are weak organic acids or bases that have different colors in their protonated and deprotonated states. Because they are highly colored, indicators can be used in low concentrations and therefore do not significantly alter the equivalence point. The indicator must always be a weaker acid or base than the acid or base being titrated; otherwise, the indicator would be titrated first! The point at which the indicator actually changes color is not the equivalence point but rather the **end point.** If the indicator is chosen correctly and the titration is performed well, the volume difference (and therefore the error) between the end point and the equivalence point is usually small and may be corrected for, or simply ignored.

Bridge

This formula should remind you of Chapter 9 . . . if not, turn back and take a look!

Bridge

A useful set of compounds (indicators) will change color as it goes between its conjugate acid and base forms:

H–Indicator ⟷ H⁺ + Indicator⁻
(color 1)   (color 2)

This allows us to use it to follow a titration and we can see that since it is an equilibrium process that we can apply Le Châtelier's principle. Adding H⁺ shifts equilibrium to left. Adding OH⁻ removes H⁺ and therefore shifts equilibrium to the right.

Acid-base titrations can be performed for different combinations of strong and weak acids and bases. The most useful combinations are strong acid/strong base, weak acid/strong base, and weak base/strong acid. Weak acid/weak base titrations can be done but are not usually accurate (and therefore almost never performed) because the pH curve for the titration of a weak acid and weak base lacks the sharp change that normally indicates the equivalence point. Furthermore, indicators are less useful because the pH change is more gradual.

STRONG ACID AND STRONG BASE

Let's consider the titration of 10 mL of a 0.1 N solution of HCl with a 0.1 N solution of NaOH. Plotting the pH of the reaction solution versus the quantity of NaOH added gives the following curve:

Figure 10.1

> **Key Concept**
>
> Our tug-of-war analogy for a bond between two atoms can be recycled in a different way with titrations. Whichever is stronger (our acid or our base) will determine the equivalence point for the titration. Here they are equal so the equivalence point is at a neutral pH.

Because HCl is a strong acid and NaOH is a strong base, the equivalence point of the titration will be at pH 7 and the solution will be neutral. Note that the end point shown is close to, but not exactly equal to, the equivalence point; selection of a better indicator, one that changes colors at, say, pH 8, would have given a better approximation. Still, the amount of error introduced by the use of an indicator that changes color around pH 11 rather than, say, pH 8 is not especially significant: a mere fraction of a milliliter of excess NaOH solution.

In the early part of the curve (when little base has been added), the acidic species predominates, and so the addition of small amounts of base will not appreciably change either the $[OH^-]$ or the pH. Similarly, in the last part of the titration curve (when an excess of base has been added), the addition of small amounts of base will not change the $[OH^-]$ significantly, and the pH remains relatively constant. The addition of base most alters the concentrations of H^+ and OH^- near the equivalence point, and thus the pH changes most drastically in that region. *The equivalence point for strong acid/strong base titration is always at pH 7 (for monovalent species).*

If you are using a pH meter so that you can chart the change in pH as a function of volume of titrant added, you can make a good approximation of the equivalence point by locating the midpoint of the region of the curve with the steepest slope.

WEAK ACID AND STRONG BASE

Titration of a weak acid, HA (e.g., CH_3COOH), with a strong base, such as NaOH, produces the following titration curve:

Figure 10.2

Key Concept

Note that any monoprotic weak acid titrated with a strong base will give a similar curve. The exact pH of the equivalence point depends on the identity of the weak acid, but the "tug-of-war" rule tells us it will be above 7.

Let's compare Figure 10.2 with Figure 10.1. The first difference we should notice is that the initial pH of the weak acid solution is greater than the initial pH of the strong acid solution. This makes sense because we know that weak acids don't dissociate to the same degree that strong acids do; therefore, the concentration of H_3O^+ will generally be lower (and pH will be higher) in a solution of weak acid. The second difference we should catch is the shapes of the curves. The pH curve for the weak acid/strong base titration shows a faster rise in pH for given additions of base. The pH changes most significantly early on in the titration, and the equivalence point is in the basic range. The third difference we should notice is the position of the equivalence point. While the equivalence point for strong acid/strong base titration is pH 7, the equivalence point for weak acid/strong base is above 7 (in the basic range). This is because the reaction between the weak acid (HA) and strong base (OH^-) produces a stronger conjugate base (A^-) and a weaker conjugate acid (H_2O). This produces a greater concentration of hydroxide ions than that of hydrogen ions at equilibrium (due to the common ion effect on the auto-ionization of water). *The equivalence point for weak acid/strong base titration is always in the basic range of the pH scale.*

WEAK BASE AND STRONG ACID

The appearance of the titration curve for a weak base titrand and strong acid titrant will look like the "inversion" of the curve for a weak acid titrand and strong base titrant. The initial pH will be in the basic range (typical range: pH 10–12) and will demonstrate a fairly quick drop in pH for additions of the strong acid. The equivalence point will be in the acidic pH range because the reaction between the weak base and strong acid will produce a stronger conjugate acid and weaker conjugate base. The stronger conjugate acid will result in an equilibrium state with a concentration of hydrogen ions greater than that of the hydroxide ions. *The equivalence point for weak base/strong acid titration is always in the acidic range of the pH scale.*

POLYVALENT ACIDS AND BASES

The titration curve for a polyvalent acid or base looks different from that for a monovalent acid or base. Figure 10.3 shows the titration of Na_2CO_3 with HCl in which the divalent (the term diprotic is equivalent) acid H_2CO_3 is the ultimate product.

Figure 10.3

In region I, little acid has been added and the predominant species is CO_3^{2-}. In region II, more acid has been added and the predominant species are CO_3^{2-} and HCO_3^-, in relatively equal concentrations. The flat part of the curve is the first buffer region (see next section), corresponding to the pK_a of HCO_3^- ($K_a = 5.6 \times 10^{-11}$ implies $pK_a = 10.25$).

Region III contains the equivalence point, at which all of the CO_3^{2-} is finally titrated to HCO_3^-. As the curve illustrates, a rapid change in pH occurs at the equivalence point; in the latter part of region III, the predominant species is HCO_3^-.

In region IV, the acid has neutralized approximately half of the HCO_3^-, and now H_2CO_3 and HCO_3^- are in roughly equal concentrations. This flat region is the second buffer region of the titration curve, corresponding to the pK_a of H_2CO_3 ($K_a = 4.3 \times 10^{-7}$

implies pK_a = 6.37). In region V, the equivalence point for the entire titration is reached, as all of the HCO_3^- is finally converted to H_2CO_3. Again, a rapid change in pH is observed near the equivalence point as acid is added.

The titrations of the acidic and basic amino acids (which have acidic or basic side chains, respectively) will show curves similar to the one shown in Figure 10.3. But rather than two equivalence points, there will in fact be three: one corresponding to the titration of the carboxylic acid and a second corresponding to the titration of the amino acid, both of which are attached to the central carbon, and a third corresponding either to the acidic or basic side chain.

BUFFERS

A **buffer solution** consists of a mixture of a weak acid and its salt (which consists of its conjugate base and a cation), or a mixture of a weak base and its salt (which consists of its conjugate acid and an anion). Two examples of buffers that are common in the laboratory and commonly tested on the MCAT are: a solution of acetic acid (CH_3COOH) and its salt, sodium acetate ($CH_3COO^-\ Na^+$); and a solution of ammonia (NH_3) and its salt, ammonium chloride ($NH_4^+Cl^-$). The acetic acid/sodium acetate solution is an acid buffer and the ammonium chloride/ammonia solution is a base buffer. Buffer solutions have the useful property of resisting changes in pH when small amounts of strong acid or base are added. Consider a buffer solution of acetic acid and sodium acetate (the sodium ion has not been included because it is not involved in the acid-base reaction):

$$CH_3COOH\ (aq) + H_2O\ (l) \leftrightarrow H_3O^+\ (aq) + CH_3COO^-\ (aq)$$

When a small amount of strong base such as NaOH is added to the buffer, the OH^- ions from the NaOH react with the H^+ ions present in the solution; subsequently, more acetic acid dissociates (the system shifts to the right), restoring the $[H^+]$. The weak acid component of the buffer acts to neutralize the strong base that has been added. The resulting increase in the concentration of the acetate ion (the conjugate base) does not yield as large an increase in hydroxide ions as the unbuffered strong base would. Thus, the addition of the strong base does not result in a significant increase in $[OH^-]$ and does not appreciably change pH. Likewise, when a small amount of HCl is added to the buffer, H^+ ions from the HCl react with the acetate ions to form acetic acid. Acetic acid is weaker than the added hydrochloric acid (which has been neutralized by the acetate ions), so the increased concentration of acetic acid does not significantly contribute to the hydrogen ion concentration in the solution. Because the buffer maintains $[H^+]$ at relatively constant values, the pH of the solution is relatively unchanged.

In the human body, one of the most important buffers is the H_2CO_3/HCO_3^- conjugate pair in the plasma compartment of the blood. $CO_2\ (g)$, one of the waste products of

1. **The oxidation number of free elements is zero.** For example, the atoms in N_2, P_4, S_8, and He all have oxidation numbers of zero.

2. **The oxidation number for a monatomic ion is equal to the charge of ion.** For example, the oxidation numbers for Na^+, Cu^{2+}, Fe^{3+}, Cl^-, and N^{3-} are +1, +2, +3, –1, and –3, respectively.

3. **The oxidation number of each Group IA element in a compound is +1. The oxidation number of each Group IIA element in a compound is +2.**

4. **The oxidation number of each Group VIIA element in a compound is –1, except when combined with an element of higher electronegativity.** For example, in HCl, the oxidation number of Cl is –1; in HOCl, however, the oxidation number of Cl is +1.

5. **The oxidation number of hydrogen is –1 in compounds with less electronegative elements than hydrogen (Groups IA and IIA).** Examples include NaH and CaH_2. The more common oxidation number of hydrogen is +1.

6. **In most compounds, the oxidation number of oxygen is –2.** This is not the case, however, in molecules such OF_2. Here, because F is more electronegative than O, the oxidation number of oxygen is +2. Also, in peroxides such as BaO_2, the oxidation number of O is –1 instead of –2 because of the structure of the peroxide ion, $[O–O]^{2-}$. (Note that Ba, a Group IIA element, cannot be a +4 cation.)

7. **The sum of the oxidation numbers of all the atoms present in a neutral compound is zero. The sum of the oxidation numbers of the atoms present in a polyatomic ion is equal to the charge of the ion.** Thus, for SO_4^{2-} the sum of the oxidation numbers must be –2.

MCAT Expertise

Don't forget that you have the periodic table available to you on Test Day, so use it to organize your thoughts with regard to these rules rather than memorizing these on their own. Beware of transition metals but realize we can often figure their oxidation by default.

Key Concept

The conventions of formula writing put cation first and anion second. Thus NaH implies H^- while HCl implies H^+. So, use the way the compound is written on the MCAT along with the periodic table to help you determine oxidation states.

Example: Assign oxidation numbers to the atoms in the following reaction in order to determine the oxidized and reduced species and the oxidizing and reducing agents.

$$SnCl_2 + PbCl_4 \rightarrow SnCl_4 + PbCl_2$$

Solution: All these species are neutral, so the oxidation numbers of each compound must add up to zero. In $SnCl_2$, because there are two chlorines present and chlorine has an oxidation number of –1, Sn must have an oxidation number of +2. Similarly, the oxidation number of Sn in $SnCl_4$ is +4; the oxidation number of Pb is +4 in $PbCl_4$ and +2 in $PbCl_2$. Notice that the oxidation number of Sn goes from +2 to +4; it loses electrons and thus is oxidized, making it the reducing agent. Because the oxidation number of Pb has decreased from +4 to +2, it has gained electrons and been reduced. Pb is the oxidizing agent. The sum of the charges on both sides of the reaction is equal to zero, so charge has been conserved.

BALANCING REDOX REACTIONS

Okay, okay. We know you don't like balancing redox reactions. We know that there are many steps involved and that it can sometimes be difficult to remember how to balance not only mass but charge as well. And we recognize the unfortunate fact that we've just presented you with seven rules of assigning oxidation numbers to understand and remember. And now we're giving you five steps to remember. And—hey, don't think we didn't just catch you rolling your eyes! Sigh all you want, but the truth of the matter is, the process of balancing redox reactions is tested on the MCAT. We might suggest that balancing redox reactions is sort of like balancing a checkbook, but we are hesitant to do so for at least two reasons: 1) balancing a checkbook isn't exactly "fun," and 2) aside from accountants (for whom it is simply part of their nature), we don't know anyone who actually balances his checkbook.

By assigning oxidation numbers to the reactants and products, you can determine how many moles of each species are required for conservation of charge and mass, which is necessary to balance the equation. To balance a redox reaction, both the net charge and the number of atoms must be equal on both sides of the equation. The most common method for balancing redox equations is the **half-reaction method,** also known as the **ion-electron method,** in which the equation is separated into two half-reactions—the oxidation part and the reduction part. Each half-reaction is balanced separately, and they are then added to give a balanced overall reaction. As we review the steps involved, let's consider a redox reaction between $KMnO_4$ and HI in an acidic solution.

$$MnO_4^- + I^- \rightarrow I_2 + Mn^{2+}$$

Step 1: Separate the two half-reactions.

$$I^- \rightarrow I_2$$
$$MnO_4^- \rightarrow Mn^{2+}$$

Step 2: Balance the atoms of each half-reaction. First, balance all atoms except H and O. Next, in an acidic solution, add H_2O to balance the O atoms and then add H^+ to balance the H atoms. (In a basic solution, use OH^- and H_2O to balance the Os and Hs.)

To balance the iodine atoms, place a coefficient of 2 before the I^- ion.

$$2 I^- \rightarrow I_2$$

For the permanganate half-reaction, Mn is already balanced. Next, balance the oxygens by adding $4H_2O$ to the right side.

$$MnO_4^- \rightarrow Mn^{2+} + 4H_2O$$

MCAT Expertise

Methodical, step-by-step approaches like this one are great for the MCAT. Most often, you will not have to get through all of these steps before you can narrow down your answer choices. Often you will be able to find the correct answer halfway through the steps.

THE EFFECT OF CONCENTRATION ON EMF

So far, we have considered the calculation of cell EMF only under standard conditions (all the ionic species are 1 M and all gases are at a pressure of 1 atm). However, electrochemical cells may have ionic concentrations that are greater or lesser than 1 M. In fact, for the concentration cell, the concentrations of the ion in the two compartments must be different, even if one of them is 1 M, in order for there to be a voltage and current. Concentration does have an effect on the EMF of a cell: EMF varies with the changing concentrations of the species involved. It can be determined by the use of the **Nernst equation**:

$$E_{cell} = E^\circ_{cell} - \left(\frac{RT}{nF} \right)(\ln Q)$$

where Q is the reaction quotient for the reaction at a given point in time. For example, for the following reaction:

$$aA + bB \rightarrow cC + dD$$

the reaction quotient can be calculated as:

$$Q = \frac{[C]^c[D]^d}{[A]^a[B]^b}$$

Although the expression for the reaction quotient Q has two terms for the concentrations of reactants and two terms for the concentrations of products, you need to remember that only the species in solution are included. When considering the case of the Daniell cell, for example, we need to think about which species of the redox reaction are in solution. Upon oxidation, the resulting cation will enter into solution, so the product concentration is the concentration of the oxidized species. Because the electrons are captured by the cations that surround the cathode in the reduction half-reaction, these cations are the reactants of the redox reaction, and so the reactant concentration is the concentration of the species that gets reduced.

The EMF of a cell can be measured by a **voltmeter.** A **potentiometer** is a kind of voltmeter that draws no current, and gives a more accurate reading of the difference in potential between two electrodes.

EMF AND THE EQUILIBRIUM CONSTANT (K_{eq})

For reactions in solution, ΔG° can determined in another manner, as follows:

$$\Delta G^\circ = -RT \ln K_{eq}$$

where R is the gas constant 8.314 J/(K $\bullet$ mol), T is the absolute temperature in K, and K_{eq} is the equilibrium constant for the reaction.

Combining the two equations for standard free energy change (above), we see that:

$$\Delta G^\circ = -nFE^\circ\text{cell} = -RT \ln K_{eq}$$

or simply:

$$nFE^\circ_{\;cell} = RT \ln K_{eq}$$

If the values for n, T, and K_{eq} are known, then the E° cell for the redox reaction can be readily calculated. On the MCAT, you will not be expected to calculate (or even approximate) natural log values in your head. That being said, these equations will still be tested, but in a more conceptual way. Analysis of the equations show us that for redox reactions that have equilibrium constants less than 1 (which tells us that the equilibrium state favors the reactants), the E°_{cell} will be negative, because the natural log of any number less than 1 is negative. These properties are characteristic of electrolytic cells, which house nonspontaneous redox reactions. If the K_{eq} for the redox reaction is greater than 1 (which tells us that the equilibrium state favors the products), the E°_{cell} will be positive, because the natural log of any number greater than 1 is positive. These properties are characteristic of galvanic cells, which house spontaneous redox reactions. If the K_{eq} is equal to 1 (which tells us that the concentrations of the reactants and products are equal at equilibrium), the E°_{cell} will be equal to zero, because, by definition of standard conditions (all ionic species at the same concentration, 1 M), the reaction is already at equilibrium. An easy way to remember this is $E^\circ_{cell} = 0$ V for any concentration cell, because, by definition, the equilibrium state of a concentration cell is when the concentrations of the ion in the two half-cells are equal ($K_{eq} = 1$ for concentration cell).

Key Concept

If E°_{cell} is positive, ln K is positive. This means that K must be greater than one, and that the equilibrium lies toward the right, i.e., products are favored.

Conclusion

In this chapter we covered the essential MCAT topics of redox reactions and electrochemistry. We reviewed the rules for assigning oxidation numbers to help us keep track of the movement of electrons from the species that are oxidized (reducing agents) to the species that are reduced (oxidizing agents). We also covered the sequence of steps involved in balancing redox reactions through the half-reaction method, and the properties and behavior of the different types of electrochemical cells. Galvanic cells rely on spontaneous redox reactions to produce current and supply energy. The concentration cell is a special type of galvanic cell for which the current is dependent upon an ion concentration gradient rather than a difference in reduction potential between two chemically distinct electrodes. Electrolytic cells rely on external voltage sources to drive a nonspontaneous redox reaction called electrolysis. Finally, we considered the thermodynamics of the different cell types.

Galvanic and concentration cells have positive EMFs and negative free energy changes. Electrolytic cells have negative EMFs and positive free changes.

Without further delay, we want to offer you our heartiest congratulations for completing this review of general chemistry for the MCAT. The hard work, time, and energy you have invested in a careful, thorough, and thoughtful review of the topics covered within the pages of this book will pay off in points on Test Day, you can be sure of that. We hope that we have been successful in meeting our goals in writing these review notes: to assess the general concepts and principles essential to answering correctly the general chemistry questions on the MCAT; to guide you in the development of critical thinking skills necessary for analyzing passages, question stems, and answer choices; and to provide holistic preparation for your Test Day experience. In addition to all of these, we had in mind the particular goals of helping you relate the science to your everyday life experiences and future experiences as a physician, demystify it, and have some fun in the process. We are grateful for the opportunity to partner with you in your journey to success on the MCAT and, beyond that, success in your medical education and future practice as a great physician!

CONCEPTS TO REMEMBER

☐ Oxidation is loss of electrons; reduction is gain of electrons (OIL RIG). Oxidation and reduction always occur as paired of reactions, in accordance with the law of conservation of charge.

☐ The oxidizing agent is the chemical species that causes another species to be oxidized and is itself reduced. The reducing agent is the chemical species that causes another species to be reduced and is itself oxidized. Assign oxidation numbers to identify the oxidizing and reducing agents.

☐ Redox reactions can be balanced by the half-reaction method:

  — Separate the half-reactions.
  — Balance the atoms in each half-reaction.
  — Balance the charges in each half-reaction.
  — Add the half-reactions.
  — Confirm balance of mass and charge in redox reaction.

☐ There are two basic types of electrochemical cells: galvanic (voltaic) cells and electrolytic cells. Concentration cells are a special type of galvanic cell.

☐ Galvanic cells have spontaneous redox reactions, generate current, and supply energy. The ΔG is negative and the E_{cell} is positive.

☐ Concentration cells have spontaneous redox reactions, generate current, and supply energy. Current is dependent upon ion concentration gradient, not the difference in reduction potential between two different electrodes. The $\Delta G°$ and the $E°_{cell}$ are both 0, because the current ceases when the concentrations of the ion are equal in both compartments.

☐ Electrolytic cells have nonspontaneous redox reactions, require external voltage to generate current, and consume energy. The ΔG is positive and the E_{cell} is negative.

☐ Reduction potential, measured in volts (V), is a measure of a chemical species' tendency to be reduced (gain electrons) relative to the standard hydrogen electrode (SHE). The higher the reduction potential, the greater the tendency to gain electrons and be reduced.

☐ The standard EMF of a cell is the difference between the standard reduction potential of the cathode minus the standard reduction potential of the anode.

☐ The Nernst equation is useful for calculating E_{cell} for all ion concentrations.

EQUATIONS TO REMEMBER

☐ $EMF° = E°_{cath} - E°_{anode} = E°_{red} + E°_{ox}$

☐ $\Delta G = -nFE_{cell}$ and $\Delta G° = -nFE°_{cell}$

☐ $E_{cell} = E°_{cell} - \left(\dfrac{RT}{nF}\right)(\ln Q)$

☐ $\Delta G° = -RT \ln K_{eq}$

☐ $\Delta G° = -nFE°cell = -RT \ln K_{eq}$ or $nFE°_{cell} = RT \ln K_{eq}$

Practice Questions

1. An electrolytic cell is filled with water. Which of the following will move toward the cathode of such a cell?

   I. H^+ ions

   II. O^{2-} ions

   III. Electrons

   A. I only

   B. II only

   C. I and III

   D. II and III

2. Consider the following data in Table 1:

Reaction	Reduction Potential
$Hg^{2+} + 2e^- \longrightarrow Hg$	+0.85 V
$Cu^+ + e^- \longrightarrow Cu$	+0.52 V
$Zn^{2+} + 2e^- \longrightarrow Zn$	−0.76 V
$Al^{3+} + 3e^- \longrightarrow Al$	−1.66 V

   The anode of a certain galvanic cell is composed of copper. Which of the metals from the data table can be used at the cathode?

   A. Hg

   B. Al

   C. Zn

   D. None of the above

3. Consider the following equation:

   $$3Na\ (s) + H_3N\ (aq) \rightarrow Na_3N\ (s) + H_2\ (g)$$

   Which species acts as an oxidizing agent?

   A. H^+

   B. H_2N

   C. Na

   D. Na^+

4. How many electrons are involved in the following unbalanced reaction?

   $$Cr_2O_7^{2-} + H^+ + e^- \rightarrow Cr^{2+} + H_2O$$

   A. 2

   B. 8

   C. 12

   D. 16

Questions 5 and 6 refer to the following two half-reactions:

$$O_2 + 4H^+ + 4e^- \rightarrow 2H_2O \qquad +1.23\ V\ (Reaction\ 1)$$
$$PbO_2 + 4H^+ + 2e^- \rightarrow Pb^{2+} + 2H_2O \qquad +1.46\ V\ (Reaction\ 2)$$

5. If the two half-reactions combine to form a spontaneous system, what is the net balanced equation of the full reaction?

   A. $2PbO_2 + 4H^+ \rightarrow 2Pb^{2+} + O_2 + 2H_2O$

   B. $PbO_2 \rightarrow Pb^{2+} + O_2 + 2e^-$

   C. $Pb^{2+} + O_2 + 2H_2O \rightarrow 2PbO_2 + 4H^+$

   D. $Pb^{2+} + O_2 + 2e^- \rightarrow PbO_2$

6. Find the standard potential of the following reaction:

$$Pb^{2+} + O_2 + 2H_2O \rightarrow 2PbO_2 + 4H^+$$

A. +0.23 V
B. −0.23 V
C. −1.69 V
D. +2.69 V

7. Rusting occurs due to the oxidation-reduction reaction of iron with environmental oxygen:

$$4Fe\ (s) + 3O_2\ (g) \rightarrow 2Fe_2O_3\ (s)$$

Some metals, such as copper, are unlikely to react with oxygen. Which of the following best explains this observation?

A. Iron has a more positive reduction potential, making it more likely to donate electrons to oxygen.
B. Iron has a more positive reduction potential, making it more likely to accept electrons from oxygen.
C. Iron has a less positive reduction potential, making it more likely to donate electrons to oxygen.
D. Iron has a less positive reduction potential, making it more likely to accept electrons from oxygen.

8. Lithium aluminum hydride ($LiAlH_4$) is often used in laboratories because of its tendency to donate a hydride ion. Which of the following properties does $LiAlH_4$ exhibit?

A. Strong reducing agent
B. Strong oxidizing agent
C. Strong acid
D. Strong base

9. If the value of $E°_{cell}$ is known, what other data is needed to calculate ΔG?

A. Equilibrium constant
B. Reaction quotient
C. Temperature of the system
D. Number of moles of electrons transferred

10. Which of the following compounds is least likely to be found in the salt bridge of a galvanic cell?

A. NaCl
B. SO_3
C. $MgSO_3$
D. NH_4NO_3

11. What is the oxidation number of chlorine in NaClO?

A. −1
B. 0
C. +1
D. +2

12. Which of the following is most likely to increase the rate of an electrolytic reaction?

A. Increasing the resistance in the circuit
B. Increasing the volume of electrolyte
C. Increasing the current
D. Increasing the pH

13. The following electronic configurations represent elements in their neutral form. Which element is the strongest oxidizing agent?

A. $1s^2 2s^2 p^6 3s^2 p^6 4s^2$
B. $1s^2 2s^2 p^6 3s^2 p^6 4s^2 3d^5$
C. $1s^2 2s^2 p^6 3s^2 p^6 4s^2 3d^{10} 4p^1$
D. $1s^2 2s^2 p^6 3s^2 p^6 4s^2 3d^5 4p^5$

Small Group Questions

1. How can a halogen have a positive oxidation number?

2. When adding standard potentials, why are we instructed not to multiply them by molar coefficients?

Explanations to Practice Questions

1. C

In an electrolytic cell, ionic compounds are broken up into their constituents; the cations (positively charged ions) migrate toward the cathode and the anions (negatively charged ions) migrate toward the anode. In this case, the cations are H^+ ions (protons), so option I is correct. In order to balance charge, electrons are transported from the anode to the cathode, meaning that option III is also correct. Option II is incorrect for two reasons. First, it's unlikely that the anions would be O^{2-} rather than OH^-. Second, these anions would flow to the anode, not the cathode.

2. A

Oxidation occurs at the anode and reduction occurs at the cathode. Since Cu is at the anode, it must be oxidized. Its standard reduction potential is +0.52 V, so its standard oxidation potential is –0.52 V. The half-reaction potentials in a feasible galvanic cell must add up to a value greater than 0, so we can answer this question by adding the oxidation potential of copper to the reduction potentials of the other metals and finding a reasonable match.

Mercury has a reduction potential of 0.85 V, which is enough to outweigh the potential contributed by copper (–0.52 V). The cell's EMF would be +0.33 V. Zinc and aluminum both have negative reduction potentials, so the overall potential of the cell will be even lower than that of copper (–1.28 V and –2.18 V, respectively). Zinc and aluminum would only be viable options if we were dealing with an electrolytic cell.

3. A

The oxidizing agent is the species that is reduced in any given equation. In this problem, two H^+ ions from H_3N are reduced to one neutral H_2 atom. H_3N is not the reducing agent because the H^+ ions and the N^{3-} ions are independent of one another in solution.

4. B

First, let's balance the equation, first making sure all the atoms are present in equal quantities on both sides.

$$Cr_2O_7^{2-} + \underline{14}H^+ + e^- \rightarrow \underline{2}Cr^{2+} + \underline{7}H_2O$$

Now, let's adjust the number of electrons to balance the charge. Currently, the left side has a charge of +12 (–2 from dichromate and +14 from protons). The right side has a charge of +4 (+2 from each chromium cation). To decrease the charge on the left side from +12 to +4, we should add 8 electrons.

$$Cr_2O_7^{2-} + 14H^+ + \underline{8}e^- \rightarrow 2Cr^{2+} + 7H_2O$$

5. A

Both half-reactions are written as reductions, so one of the two must be reversed to perform oxidation. If a reaction represents a spontaneous process, then the overall potential must be positive. The only way to create a spontaneous oxidation-reduction system is by reversing Reaction 1 to produce a positive net potential.

$$2H_2O \rightarrow O_2 + 4H^+ + 4e^- \qquad -1.23 \text{ V (oxidation)}$$

The half-reactions are each already balanced for mass and charge. Before we add them together, we must make sure each of them transfers the same number of electrons. Multiply all of Reaction 2's coefficients by 2, so that both reactions transfer 4 moles of electrons.

$$2H_2O \rightarrow O_2 + 4H^+ + 4e^- \qquad -1.23 \text{ V (oxidation)}$$
$$2PbO_2 + 8H^+ + 4e^- \rightarrow 2Pb^{2+} + 4H_2O \quad +1.46 \text{ V (reduction)}$$

Now, add the two reactions together.

$$2H_2O + 2PbO_2 + 8H^+ + 4e^- \rightarrow$$
$$O_2 + 4H^+ + 4e^- + 2Pb^{2+} + 4H_2O$$

1) **Look at the energy differences between the starting material and the product(s) as well as the differences between the starting material and the transition state leading to each product.**

   Notice that the energy of **C** is lower than that of **B.** Therefore, it is the more thermodynamically stable product.

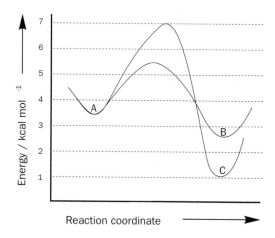

   Reaction coordinate

   The rate of formation of each product is determined by the difference in energy between the starting material **A** and the top of the "hump" leading to each product. Because this distance is lower for the formation of **B,** it forms faster.

2) **Note that the difference in energy between the starting material and the product(s) determines the ratio of products to reactants at equilibrium.**

   $$\Delta G° = -RT \ln K_{eq}$$

   This equation provides the relationship between K_{eq} and $\Delta G°$. We need to rearrange it to solve for K_{eq}.

   $$K_{eq} = e^{\frac{-\Delta G°}{RT}}$$

   Note that $\Delta G° \approx 1{,}000 - 3{,}500 = -2{,}500$ cal mol^{-1}, from the diagram, and R = 1.99 cal (mol K)$^{-1}$ $\approx$ 2 cal (mol K)$^{-1}$, and $T = 298 \approx 300$ K.

   $$K_{eq} = e^{\frac{-\Delta G°}{RT}} = e^{\frac{-(-2500)}{(2)(300)}} = e^{\frac{2500}{600}}$$

   Let's say 2,500/600 is about equal to 4, and $e = 2.7818 \approx 3$.

   $$K_{eq} = e^4 = 81 = \frac{[C]}{[A]}$$

   Note that a negative $\Delta G°$ gives more product than reactant, as you would expect for a spontaneous reaction.

3) Consider what role(s) the addition of a catalyst might play.

Remember: A catalyst is something that speeds up a reaction and is not consumed during a reaction. If it speeds up a reaction, it lowers the "hump" in the reaction profile. So, we could increase the rate of formation of C by adding a catalyst to that reaction, making the rate closer to the rate of formation of B.

---

4) Consider the effects of temperature on the reaction(s).

At high temperatures for long times, **A** has the energy to go back and forth over and over again between **B** and **C.** Then, over time, the lowest energy product **C** would predominate, just as rolling a ball down a hill would cause it to fall to the lowest location.

Between the two products, **B** will form much faster than **C** because its energy of activation (height of the "hump") is lower. At low temperatures, the products won't have the energy to go back over the hill to get to **A,** so the faster-forming product will predominate (i.e., **B**).

Similar Questions

1) What would be the ratio of **B** to **A** at equilibrium?

2) If a catalyst were added to the reaction of **A** going to **C**, as in step 3 above, would the energies of **A** and **C** be changed as a result? Why or why not?

3) There are actually intermediates involved in the reactions producing both **B** and **C**. These intermediates are shown below. Sketch how each reaction profile would look, including the involvement of these intermediates. Be sure to indicate which intermediate is relatively more stable.

Key Concepts

Chapter 6

Thermochemistry

Gibbs free energy

Enthalpy

Entropy

Equilibrium constant, K_{eq}

Reaction quotient, Q

$\Delta G = \Delta H - T\Delta S$ (kJ/mol)

$\Delta G° = -RT \ln K_{eq}$ (kJ/mol)

$\Delta G = \Delta G° + RT \ln Q$ (kJ/mol)

Takeaways

Two equations should get you through nearly any thermochemistry question. Remember to round your numbers and to predict the ballpark for your answers wherever possible.

Things to Watch Out For

Pay close attention to the units used.

Thermodynamic Equilibrium

The reaction $2NO(g) + Cl_2(g) \rightarrow 2NOCl(g)$ adheres to the following thermodynamic data:

ΔH	−77.1 kJ/mol
ΔS	−121 J/K
ΔG	−44.0 kJ/mol
K_{eq}	1.54×10^7

Suppose that, in equilibrium, NO exerts 0.6 atm of pressure and Cl_2 adds 0.3 atm; find the partial pressure of NOCl in this equilibrium. Also, find the temperature at which the thermodynamic data in the table were reported. K_{eq} is related to K_p by the following equation: $K_p = K_{eq}(RT)^{\Delta n}$ where Δn is the change in number of moles of gas evolved as the reaction moves forward. $(R = 8.314$ J/K · mol)

1) Find the temperature at which the thermodynamic data are true.

$\Delta G = \Delta H - T\Delta S$

$(-44$ kJ/mol$) = (-77$ kJ/mol$) - T(-0.121$ kJ/K × mol$) \rightarrow T = 273$ K

Being able to work with the equation $\Delta G = \Delta H - T\Delta S$ is absolutely crucial for Test Day. Specifically concerning the data here, because both ΔH and ΔS are negative, the reaction will become "less spontaneous" as we increase temperature. This will help narrow down our answer choices on Test Day.

MCAT Pitfall: *Notice that not all of the state functions were given in the same unit! Had you blindly put in entropy without changing its units, you would have obtained a temperature near absolute zero (0 K). At absolute zero, molecules no longer move, and it is unlikely that this reaction would have such a high equilibrium constant.*

2) Find Δn.

For the equation:

$2NO(g) + Cl_2(g) \rightarrow 2NOCl(g)$

$\Delta n = 2 - (2 + 1) = -1$

3) Find K_p.

$$K_p = K_{eq}(RT)^{\Delta n}$$
$$K_p = (1.54 \times 10^7)(8.314 \text{ J/K·mole})(273 \text{ K})^{-1}$$
$$= 6{,}785$$

Use the temperature value from step #1.

You are not responsible for memorizing the equation. However, in the MCAT, you have to be able to use a brand-new equation to solve for the answer.

---

4) Find the partial pressure.

$$K_p = \frac{\left(P_{NOCl}^{eq}\right)^2}{\left(P_{NO}^{eq}\right)^2 \left(P_{Cl_2}^{eq}\right)}$$

Plug in the given data into the reaction quotient.

$$6{,}785 = \frac{\left(P_{NOCl}^{eq}\right)^2}{(.6)^2 \cdot (.3)}$$

$$733 = \left(P_{NOCl}^{eq}\right)^2$$

$$27 \text{ atm} = P_{NOCl}^{eq}$$

Similar Questions

1) If $K_{eq} = 7.4 \times 10^{-3}$ for CH_4 (g) $+ 2H_2O$ (g) $\rightarrow CO_2$ (g) $+ 4H_2$ (g), which is more plentiful, the reactants or the products?

2) If pyrophosphoric acid ($H_4P_2O_7$) and arsenous acid (H_3AsO_3) have acid dissociation constants of 3×10^{-2} and 6.6×10^{-10}, respectively, at room temperature, find the Gibbs free energy of each dissociation reaction and determine if it is spontaneous. What does this mean for the ΔH and ΔS for these reactions?

3) A chemist is given three liquid-filled flasks, each labeled with generic thermodynamic data. She is told to put one in a cold room, to put one on a Bunsen burner, and to leave one on the benchtop—whatever conditions will best facilitate the reaction. If the flasks are labeled as follows, which flask goes where?

   A $\Delta H < 0, \Delta S > 0$

   E $\Delta H < 0, \Delta S < 0$

   P $\Delta H > 0, \Delta S > 0$

Key Concepts

Chapter 6

Hess's law:

$\Delta H_{rxn} = \Delta H_f(\text{products}) - \Delta H_f(\text{reactants})(\text{kJ/mol})$

Enthalpy

Bond dissociation energy

Combustion

Stoichiometry

$\Delta H_{rxn} = \Delta H_b (\text{reactants}) - \Delta H_b (\text{products}) (\text{kJ/mol})$

$\Delta H_{rxn} = \text{total energy input} - \text{total energy released (kJ/mol)}$

Takeaways

Consider the number of bonds before applying Hess's law. Make sure to take note of how many bonds are in a given molecule as well as how many stoichiometric equivalents of that molecule you have.

Bond Enthalpy

An unknown compound containing only carbon and hydrogen is subjected to a combustion reaction in which 2,059 kJ of heat are released. If 3 moles of CO_2 and 4 moles of steam are produced for every mole of the unknown compound reacted, find the enthalpy for a single C–H bond.

Bond	Bond Dissociation Energy (kJ/mol)
O=O	497
C=O	805
O–H	464
C–C	347

1) Write a balanced equation for the reaction.

$C_3H_8 + 5O_2 \rightleftharpoons 3CO_2 + 4H_2O$

The question stem tells us a few things about the reaction: it is combustion, the carbon source has the generic structure C_xH_y, and the products include 10 oxygen atoms, 3 carbon atoms, and 8 H atoms. To balance the reaction, we'd need those atoms on the left side, too. Thus, we find that our unknown sample is actually propane and that we need 5 O_2 molecules.

Remember: For our purposes, it is completely acceptable to have a fractional coefficient in front of a diatomic molecule. $2C_2H_4 + (7/2)O_2 \rightarrow 3H_2O + 2CO_2$ is equivalent to $4C_2H_4 + 7CO_2 \rightarrow 6H_2O + 4CO_2$.

2) Determine which bonds are broken and which are formed.

C_3H_8: 2 C–C bonds broken, 8 C–H bonds broken
$5O_2$: 5 O=O bonds broken
$3CO_2$: 6 C=O bonds formed
$4H_2O$: 8 O–H bonds formed

Combustion of C_3H_8 will break apart the carbon backbone and the C–H bonds. The carbon is in a straight chain (as opposed to cyclic or branched), so 2 C–C bonds and 8 C–H bonds are broken. For O_2, only one O=O bond is broken. However, we have 5 moles of this reactant, and thus we have 5 O=O bonds broken. Each molecule of carbon dioxide has 2 C=O bonds, but we have 3 moles of CO_2, so we have 6 C=O bonds formed. Similarly, 8 O–H bonds are formed in the 4 moles of water produced.

3) Apply Hess's law.

$\Delta H_{rxn} = \Delta H_b$ (reactants) $- \Delta H_b$ (products)

ΔH_{rxn} = total energy input $-$ total energy released

$-2{,}059 = [2(347) + 8x + 5(497)] - [6(805) + 8(464)]$

$-2{,}059 = [3{,}179 + 8x] - [8{,}542]$

$-2{,}059 + 8{,}542 - 3{,}179 = 8x$

$x = 413$ kJ/mol

Bond dissociation energy is the energy required to break a particular type of bond in one mole of gaseous molecules. Bond energies can be used to estimate the enthalpy of reaction as given by the two equations above. When we start plugging in numbers, we are given all data except for C−H bond enthalpy. We solve for this variable (x in the above equations).

Remember: *The equation $\Delta H_{rxn} = \Delta H_b$ (reactants) $- \Delta H_b$ (products) is simply a restatement of Hess's law. Bond enthalpy is for bond breaking and enthalpy of formation, of course, is for bond making. Changing ΔH_F to ΔH_b switches the signs and, thus, the order of the equation. Keep in mind that it can also be written as $\Delta H_{rxn} = \Delta H_b$ (bonds broken) $+ \Delta H_b$ (bonds formed), but you must remember to make the bond enthalpies for the products negative because forming bonds releases energy.*

4) Use Avogadro's number.

$(413$ kJ/mol$) \times [1$ mol$/(6.022 \times 10^{23}$ molecules$)]$

$= 6.86 \times 10^{-22}$ kJ/molecule

We see that 413 kJ are found in one mole of C−H bonds. One mole of a substance is equal to 6.022×10^{23} molecules. Here, we simply use that conversion factor. The result tells us that 6.86×10^{-22} kJ are stored in each C−H bond.

Things to Watch Out For

There are a number of ways to set up the equation for ΔH_{rxn}. Whatever equation you use, keep your signs straight. Remember that forming bonds releases energy, whereas breaking bonds requires energy.

Similar Questions

1) Ethanol metabolism in yeast consists of the conversion of ethanol (C_2H_5OH) to acetic acid (CH_3COOH). What is the enthalpy of the reaction if 0.1 mmol of ethanol is metabolized?

2) A second metabolic process involves the net production of 2 ATP and 2 NADH from 2 ADP and 2 NAD$^+$. If the conversion of these molecules is endothermic and adds 443.5 kJ to the overall enthalpy of the reaction, find the enthalpy for a "high-energy" phosphate bond.

3) Tristearin is oxidized in the body according to the following reaction: $2C_{57}H_{110}O_6 + 163O_2 \rightarrow 114CO_2 + 110H_2O$. If the standard enthalpy for this reaction is -34 MJ mol^{-1}, find the total enthalpy for the bonds in tristearin.

Key Concepts

Chapter 6

Hess's law:

$\Delta H_{rxn} = \Delta H_f(\text{products}) -$
$\Delta H_f(\text{reactants})$ (kJ/mol)

Heat of formation

Combustion

Heat of Formation

> The heat of combustion of glucose ($C_6H_{12}O_6$) is $-2{,}537.3$ kJ/mol. If the $\Delta H°_f$ of $CO_2(g)$ is -393.5 kJ/mol, and the $\Delta H°_f$ of $H_2O(g)$ is -241.8 kJ/mol, what is the $\Delta H°_f$ of glucose?

1) Write a balanced equation for the reaction.

Unbalanced reaction: $C_6H_{12}O_6 + O_2 \rightarrow CO_2 + H_2O$

Balanced reaction: $C_6H_{12}O_6 + 6O_2 \rightarrow 6CO_2 + 6H_2O$

The unbalanced reaction above is typical of all hydrocarbon combustion reactions. (Unless otherwise noted, presume that combustion of carbohydrates is with oxygen gas.) Begin by balancing the carbons on the left side ($6CO_2$), then balance the hydrogens on the left side ($12H_2O$), and conclude by balancing the oxygen gas on the right side ($6O_2$).

Remember: For our purposes, it is completely acceptable to have a fractional coefficient in front of a diatomic molecule. $2C_2H_4 + (7/2)O_2 \rightarrow 3H_2O + 2CO_2$ *is equivalent to* $4C_2H_4 + 7CO_2 \rightarrow 6H_2O + 4CO_2$ *but the math is simpler for the former.*

Takeaways

Always identify the balanced equation for the reaction before you begin to apply Hess's law. There is a second way of thinking about Hess's law that may be applicable in some questions as well (see previous topic). The given information in the passage and/or question stem will dictate which equation to use. Finally, recall that enthalpy is a state function, and regardless of the path you take to get from the reactants to the products, the change in enthalpy will be the same.

2) Apply Hess's law.

$\Delta H_{rxn} = \Delta H_f(\text{products}) - \Delta H_f(\text{reactants})$

$-2{,}537.3 = [6(-393.5) + 6(-241.8)] - [\Delta H_f(\text{glucose})]$

Rearranging to solve for ΔH_f(glucose):

$\Delta H_f(\text{glucose}) = 2{,}537.3 + [6(-393.5) + 6(-241.8)]$

$\Delta H_f(\text{glucose}) = 2{,}537.3 + [-2{,}361 + -1{,}450.8]$

$\Delta H_f(\text{glucose}) = 2{,}537.3 + [-3{,}811.8]$

$\Rightarrow \Delta H_f(\text{glucose}) = -1{,}274.5$

The heat of formation is defined as the heat absorbed or released during the formation of a pure substance from the elements at a constant pressure. Therefore, by definition, diatomic gases like oxygen have a heat of formation of zero. A negative heat of formation means that heat is released to form the product, whereas a positive heat of formation means that heat is required to form the product. The overall combustion reaction of glucose releases $2{,}537.3$ kJ/mol of heat.

Things to Watch Out For

At least one of the wrong answer choices for thermochemistry questions will be a result from carelessness with signs. Organized scratchwork in a stepwise fashion will facilitate avoiding this problem, but perhaps more important is maintaining the ability to approximate the answer. Only experience (a.k.a. practice!) will breed such wisdom.

Similar Questions

1) Given the ΔH_F of carbon dioxide and water, what other piece(s) of information must you have to calculate the ΔH_{comb} of ethane?

2) If the ΔH_F of acetylene is 226.6 kJ/mol, what is the ΔH_{comb} of acetylene?

3) If the ΔH_F of NaBr (s) is –359.9 kJ/mol, what is the sum of each ΔH_F of the following series of five reactions?

$$Na\,(s) \rightarrow Na\,(g) \rightarrow Na^+\,(g)$$
$$\frac{1}{2}\,Br_2\,(g) \rightarrow Br\,(g) \rightarrow Br^-\,(g)$$
$$Na^+\,(g) + Br^-\,(g) \rightarrow NaBr\,(s)$$

Key Concepts

Chapter 7

Dalton's law

$P_A = X_A P_{Total}$ (atm)

Mole fraction

$X_A = \dfrac{(\text{moles of } A)}{(\text{total \# of moles in container})}$

Partial Pressures

32 g of oxygen, 28 g of nitrogen, and 22 g of carbon dioxide are confined in a container with partial pressures of 2 atm, 2 atm and 1 atm respectively. A student added 57 g of a halogen gas to this container and observed that the total pressure increased by 3 atm. Can you identify this gas?

1) Determine the number of moles for each gas.

$MW_{oxygen} = 32$ g/mol

$MW_{nitrogen} = 28$ g/mol

$MW_{carbon\ dioxide} = 44$ g/mol

$n = \dfrac{mass}{MW}$

$n_{oxygen} = 1$ mol

$n_{nitrogen} = 1$ mol

$n_{carbon\ dioxide} = 0.5$ mol

This is a more complicated style of partial pressure questions, yet the first step is still the basic one of identifying the number of moles for each gas.

Takeaways

Partial pressure questions will require manipulation of the formulas above, so the key is to always keep track of what is given to you and what the question is asking for.

2) Solve for the relevant variable.

$P_A = X_A P_{Total}$

$X_A = \dfrac{P_A}{P_{Total}}$

$X_A = \dfrac{3}{8}$

All partial pressure questions boil down to this formula. The relevant variable here is the mole fraction of the halogen gas. The partial pressure of the gas is 3 atm, and the total pressure is 8 atm.

Things to Watch Out For

Dalton's law assumes that the gases do not react with each other.

3) Use the mole fraction X_A to solve for the number of moles and the MW of the halogen gas.

The mole fraction of a substance is the number of moles of the substance as a fraction of the total number of moles in the container:

$X_A = \dfrac{(\text{moles of } A)}{(\text{total \# of moles in container})}$

Rearranging the formula, we have # moles of $A = (X_A)$(total # of moles). Note that the total number of moles is not known, but we can express it algebraically as $2.5 + n_A$, where n_A is defined as the number of moles of A.

moles of $A = (X_A)$(total # of moles)

$$n_A = \left(\frac{3}{8}\right)(2.5 + n_A)$$
$$8n_A = 7.5 + 3n_A$$
$$5n_A = 7.5$$
$$n_A = 1.5$$
$$MW = \frac{57\,g}{1.5\,mol}$$
$$MW = 38\,g/mol$$

This MW corresponds to F_2. Of course, on Test Day you will roughly round such that 60 g = 1.5 mol and look for the halogen gas using your calculated MW of 40 g/mol. Again, the only gas possible is F_2.

Similar Questions

1) 64 g of oxygen, 14 g of nitrogen, and 66 g of carbon dioxide are confined in a container. If the total pressure is 10 atm, what is the partial pressure of each gas?

2) The partial pressure of nitrogen is 2 atm. If its mole fraction is 2/10 and the only other gas in the container is oxygen, how many moles of oxygen are in the container?

3) An unknown substance's mole fraction is 4/10. If its partial pressure is 5 atm, what is the sum pressure of all the other gases in the container?

Key Concepts

Chapter 9

Normality

Molarity

Oxidation and reduction

Concentration

Normality and Molarity

What volume of a 2.0 M solution of lithium aluminum hydride in ether is necessary to reduce 1 mole of methyl 5-cyanopentanoate to the corresponding amino alcohol? What if a 2.0 N (with respect to H^-) solution were used instead?

1) Determine the number of equivalents of reagent necessary to accomplish the desired transformation.

There are two functional groups that need to be reduced in the molecule, the nitrile and the ester.

The ester will require two moles of hydride to be reduced to the alcohol.

The nitrile will also require two moles of hydride because it proceeds through an imine intermediate.

Takeaways

The molecular formula of a molecule tells you how many equivalents of a desired reagent/atom are contained within the reagent. This is why it's important to balance reactions and draw Lewis structures correctly.

Things to Watch Out For

Be careful to distinguish between equivalents and moles. With molecules containing several equivalents of reagents, the number of equivalents and moles are not equal!

2) Compute the necessary volume of the given solution.

$$4 \text{ mol hydride} \times \left(\frac{1 \text{ mol LiAlH}_4}{4 \text{ mol hydride}} \right) = 1 \text{ mol LiAlH}_4$$

Don't forget that one mole of lithium aluminum hydride contains four moles of hydride.

$$\frac{1 \text{ mol LiAlH}_4}{(2 \text{ mol LiAlH}_4 \text{ L}^{-1})} = 0.5 \text{ L}$$

So, we'll need 500 mL of the 2.0 M solution.

$$\frac{1 \text{ mol LiAlH}_4}{(0.5 \text{ mol LiAlH}_4 \text{ L}^{-1})} = 2 \text{ L of } 2.0 \text{ } N \text{ solution}$$

With the 2.0 N solution, things get a little trickier. If the solution is 2.0 N with respect to H$^-$, that means that each liter of solution contains 2 moles of hydride, or 0.5 moles of LiAlH$_4$.

Remember: *Normality refers to equivalents per unit volume, not necessarily moles of compound per unit volume.*

Similar Questions

1) Determine the volumes necessary for the same reaction as that in the initial question if 4.0 M and 4.0 N solutions of lithium aluminum hydride were used instead.

2) If the following molecule were subjected to LiAlH$_4$ reduction as well, what would the product be? How much of the 2.0 M solution would be necessary? The 2.0 N solution?

3) Diisobutylaluminum hydride (DIBAL) is a common alternate hydride reducing agent. Its structure is shown below. How much of a 2.5 M solution would be necessary to carry out the same reaction described above? A 2.5 N solution?

Key Concepts

Chapter 9

pH

Molar solubility

Common ion effect

Le Châtelier's principle

$K_{sp} = [A^+]^x_{sat}\,[B^-]^y_{sat}$

Takeaways

The value of K_{sp} does not change when a common ion is present; it is a constant that is dependent on temperature. The molar solubility of the salt, however, does change if a common ion is present. To find the change in molar solubility due to the common ion effect, you must find the K_{sp} of the substance first.

Things to Watch Out For

Be careful when applying Le Châtelier's principle in cases of precipitation and solvation. For a solution at equilibrium (i.e., saturated), adding more solid would not shift the equilibrium to the right. More solid does not dissociate to raise the ion concentrations; the solid just piles up at the bottom.

Molar Solubility

The molar solubility of iron(III) hydroxide in pure water at 25°C is 9.94×10^{-10} mol/L. How would the substance's molar solubility change if placed in an aqueous solution of pH 10.0 at 25°C?

1) Identify the balanced equation for the dissociation reaction.

The generic dissociation reaction may be expressed as:

$$A_xB_y(s) \rightarrow xA^+(aq) + yB^-(aq)$$

Plugging in for iron(III) hydroxide, the reaction expression is:

$$Fe(OH)_3(s) \rightarrow Fe^{+3}(aq) + 3OH^-(aq)$$

This step allows us to see how many moles of ions are added to the solution per mole dissolved.

2) Find the K_{sp} expression for the dissociation reaction.

Generic: $K_{sp} = [xA^+]^x_{sat}\,[yB^-]^y_{sat}$

$Fe(OH)_3$: $K_{sp} = [Fe^{+3}]\,[OH^-]^3$

K_{sp} is merely an equilibrium constant just like K, and it is given the special name "solubility product" because it tells us how soluble a solid is.

Recall that the concentrations are those at equilibrium, thus the solution is saturated. A saturated solution contains the maximum concentration of dissolved solute.

Remember: Like all Ks, a substance's K_{sp} varies only with temperature.

3) Calculate molar solubility of each product by assuming that you're starting with x mols of reactant.

$$x \text{ mol } Fe(OH)_3 \rightarrow x \text{ mol } Fe^{+3} + 3x \text{ mol } OH^-$$

Use the balanced equation from step 1 to determine the appropriate coefficients. For each mole of iron hydroxide dissolved, four ions are created: one Fe^{+3} and three OH^-.

4) Plug the molar solubility for each product into the K_{sp} equation:

$Fe(OH)_3$: $K_{sp} = [Fe^{+3}] [OH^-]^3$

$K_{sp} = [x] [3x]^3 = 27x^4$ ($x = 9.94 \times 10^{-10}$)

$K_{sp} = 27(9.94 \times 10^{-10})^4 = 2.64 \times 10^{-35}$

Simply plug in the coefficients from step 3 into the K_{sp} equation. The molar solubility, x, was given in the question stem. Thus, to calculate K_{sp}, plug in 9.94×10^{-10}. Now that we are armed with the K_{sp}, we can find the change in molar solubility due to the common ion.

---

5) If a common ion is present in a solution, it must also be accounted for in the K_{sp} equation:

$Fe(OH)_3$: $K_{sp} = [Fe^{+3}] [OH^-]^3$

$2.64 \times 10^{-35} = x(3x + 10^{-4})^3 \approx x(10^{-4})^3$

$2.64 \times 10^{-35} = x10^{-12}$

$x = 2.64 \times 10^{-23}$

A solution of pH 10.0 has an OH^- concentration of 10^{-4}. Although iron hydroxide will also contribute to the solution's total concentration of OH^-, its contribution will be negligible relative to the 10^{-4} already present in solution; thus, when plugging in for the $[OH^-]$, we can approximate that it equals 10^{-4}. For the pH 10.0 solution, the molar solubility is on the order of 10^{-23} mol/L, a steep decrease from the 10^{-9} in pure water. This is due to the common ion effect. Look at it from the perspective of Le Châtelier's principle: the addition of more OH^- will shift the reaction to the left, so that less iron hydroxide will dissociate.

Similar Questions

1) Given a substance's K_{sp}, how would you solve for its molar solubility in pure water? What if a common ion were also present in solution?

2) Given a table listing substances and their solubility constants, how would you determine which substance was most soluble in pure water?

3) Given that the sulfate ion can react with acid to form hydrogen sulfate, how would the molar solubility of sulfate salts be affected by varying a solution's pH?

pH and pK_a

What is the pH of the resulting solution if 4 g of sodium acetate (CH_3CO_2Na) is dissolved in 0.5 L of water? (The pK_a of acetic acid, CH_3CO_2H, is 4.74.)

1) Convert masses to concentrations.

Molecular weight of sodium acetate in $g\ mol^{-1}$: $23 + 2(12) + 3(1) + 2(16) = 82$

The concentration of a solution is usually expressed in units of moles per liter.

Choose numbers that are easy to work with, i.e., $80\ g\ mol^{-1}$ instead of $82\ g\ mol^{-1}$. Remember, you won't have a calculator on Test Day! Moles of sodium acetate:
$$\frac{4\ g}{80\ g\ mol^{-1}} = \frac{1}{20}\ mol = 0.05\ mol.$$

$$\text{Concentration} = \frac{0.05\ mol}{0.5\ L} = 0.1\ M$$

Remember: Moles, not grams, are the "common currency" of chemistry problems dealing with reactions. Concentration, usually in units of moles per liter, is the essential quantity for these acid-base problems.

---

2) Choose the constant that will make most sense for the reaction in question and compute its value.

Now we need to decide which constant we will use, K_a or K_b. Here's where a little common sense goes a long way. If you think about sodium acetate, you should realize that it is the conjugate base of acetic acid. Therefore, we need the value of K_b for sodium acetate. Even though we are given the pK_a of acetic acid, getting the K_b from this information is no sweat.

In water, $K_a \times K_b$ is always equal to K_w, or 10^{-14}. Take the negative logarithm of both sides.

$$-\log(K_a \times K_b) = -\log(10^{-14})$$

Remember that $\log(a \times b) = \log a + \log b$ and that $\log 10^x = x$.

$$-\log K_a + -\log K_b = -\log 10^{-14} = 14$$
$$pK_a + pK_b = 14$$

Don't forget that $-\log(\text{whatever}) = p(\text{whatever})$. We will want to find K_b because sodium acetate is the conjugate base of acetic acid.

Plug in the pK_a from above (to make our lives easier, let's say $4.74 \approx 5$).

$$pK_b = 14 - pK_a = 9$$
$$K_b = 10^{-pK_b} = 10^{-9}$$

Remember: The p-scale is a hugely important value for acid-base problems. Remember that p(something) = −log(something).

3) Write down the appropriate chemical reaction and set up a table.

Here we need to set up a table to reflect the data we've collected. This is the "putting it all together" step and is crucial.

Our table will be as follows:

	$H_2O\ (l) + CH_3CO_2^-\ (aq) \rightarrow CH_3CO_2H\ (aq) + OH^-\ (aq)$			
Initial	—	0.1	0	0
Change	—	$-x$	$+x$	$+x$
Equilibrium	—	$0.1 - x$	x	x

Initial: The idea is that we're going to take some sodium acetate, dump it into water, and see what happens. Our initial row in the table shows the concentrations that we have before any reaction takes place. That means that we'll start with the amount of sodium acetate we computed, 0.1 *M*. There's no acetic acid or hydroxide because no reaction has happened yet.

Change: Here's where all the action happens. As our acetate reacts with water, the concentration is going to decrease by some amount. We don't know what that will be yet, so let's just call it *x*. If the acetate concentration goes *down* by *x*, the concentrations of acetic acid and hydroxide must go *up* by the same amount, so we put *x*'s in their columns.

Equilibrium: This is the easy part. Just add up all of the columns above. Our completed table will look like the table at left.

*Remember: **Always, always, always** make sure that **any** chemical reaction you write down is **balanced**. This means to make sure that **mass** is balanced (the number of atoms on either side of the reaction) and that **charge** is balanced. Also, the concentration of pure liquids (e.g., water) and pure solids is never taken into account in equilibria.*

4) Plug the equilibrium concentrations from the table into the appropriate acidity or basicity expression.

$$K_b = \frac{[CH_3CO_2]_{eq}[OH^-]_{eq}}{[CH_3CO_2^-]_{eq}} = \frac{X\ X}{0.1 - X} = \frac{X^2}{0.1 - X} = 10^{-9}$$

We know that K_b is just the K_{eq} for the reaction in our table above. Plug in the numbers from the table.

Things to Watch Out For

Remember that the cardinal principle of handling computation on the MCAT is to *avoid it whenever possible* because it is so time consuming and drastically increases the chances of making a mistake. If you can't avoid doing computation, *choose numbers that are easy to work with*. So, for example, you wouldn't want to use 199.9999, you would just use 200.

5) Simplify the expression from step 4 and solve it.

Let's make our lives easier (*and* save ourselves time on Test Day) by assuming that x is much, much smaller than 0.1, so that $0.1 - x \approx 0.1$.

$$\frac{x^2}{0.1} = 10^{-9}$$
$$x^2 = (0.1)(10^{-9}) = 10^{-10}$$
$$x = 10^{-5}$$

Now why would we want to assume that x is very, very small? Well, remember that sodium acetate is a weak base because it has a K_b value. So, if it's a weak base, it won't react much with water, thus making x a very small number.

Remember: Don't forget to check the assumption we made to simplify our equation. Because $x = 10^{-5}$, which is indeed much less than 0.1 (by a factor of 10,000), our assumption holds.

---

6) Answer the question.
$$-\log[OH^-] = -\log[10^{-5}] = 5 = pOH$$
$$pH = 14 - 5 = 9$$

This step is trickier than it sounds and is where many, many mistakes are committed. Here's where attention to detail counts. You don't want to slog through all of the work above and then mess up at the end, when 99% of the work is done!

Think about what you've solved for. What is x? Well, if we look at the table, we see that x is the concentration of hydroxide. So, if we take the negative log of the hydroxide ion concentration, we get the pOH.

Remember that pH + pOH = 14. The actual pH is 8.89. So, all of our assumptions and roundings didn't affect the answer much, but saved us a lot of time in computation!

Remember: Always ask yourself whether your final answer makes sense. The MCAT isn't a computation test, it's a test of critical thinking. Here, we have a base being dissolved in water, so at the end of the day, the pH better be above 7, which it is.

Key Concepts

Chapter 10

Titration

Acids and bases

Equivalence point

Half-equivalence point

pH

Titration

Hydrazoic acid, HN_3, is a highly toxic compound that can cause death in minutes if inhaled in concentrated form. 100 mL of 0.2 M aqueous solution of HN_3 (pK_a = 4.72) is to be titrated with a 0.5 M solution of NaOH.

a) What is the pH of the HN_3 solution before any NaOH is added?

b) The *half-equivalence* point of a titration is where half the titrant necessary to get to the equivalence point has been added. How much of the NaOH solution will be needed to get to the half-equivalence point? What is the pH at the half-equivalence point?

c) What is the pH at the equivalence point?

Takeaways

Setting up the tables as shown above makes quick work of titration pH questions. Remember to make approximations and use numbers that are easy to work with in order to minimize the computation necessary to get to the answer.

1) Determine the pH before the titration.

What you need to ask yourself in each stage of this problem is which species is present, H+ or OH−, and where is it coming from? Before the titration begins, we have H+ around because, as the name of the compound suggests, hydrazoic acid is *acidic*. The major source of H+ is from the hydrazoic acid itself, so we can set up a table as follows:

H_2O (l) + HN_3(aq) → H_3O^+ (aq) + OH^-(aq)				
Initial	—	0.2	0	0
Change	—	− x	+ x	+ x
Equilibrium	—	0.2 − x	x	x

Plug in the concentrations from the table. We know the pK_a is around 5, so the K_a must be 10^{-5}. Whenever exponents or logarithms are involved, *use numbers that are easy to work with*. Make the approximation that $0.2 - x \approx 0.2$ because HN_3 is a weak acid.

$$K_a = \frac{[H_3O^+][N_3^-]}{[HN_3]} = \frac{x^2}{0.2-x} = \frac{x^2}{0.2} = 10^{-5}$$

If you must take a square root, try and get the power of 10 to be even to make matters simple. Remember from the table that x is the hydronium ion concentration.

$$x^2 = 2 \times 10^{-1} \times 10^{-5} = 2 \times 10^{-6}$$

$$\Rightarrow x = \sqrt{0.2 \times 10^{-6}} \approx 1.4 \times 10^{-3}$$

$$\Rightarrow [H_3O^+]_{eq} = 1.4 \times 10^{-3}$$

$$\Rightarrow pH = -\log[H_3O^+] = -\log(1.4 \times 10^{-3}) = 3 - \log(1.4)$$

Remember that $-\log[a \times 10^{-b}] = b - \log[a]$ = somewhere between $b - 1$ and b.

$$2 < pH < 3$$

2) Find the equivalence point and half-equivalence point.

Compute the number of moles of HN_3 that you start with.

$$\text{mol } HN_3 = 0.1 \text{ L} \times 0.2 \text{ mol L}^{-1} = 0.02 \text{ mol } HN_3$$

$$\frac{0.02 \text{ mol NaOH}}{0.5 \text{ mol L}^{-1}} = 0.04 \text{ L NaOH solution}$$

Each mole of HN_3 will react with one mole of OH^-. Therefore, the equivalence point is reached when 40 mL of the NaOH solution are added and the half-equivalence point is at $40/2 = 20$ mL. We could go through the whole rigamarole of setting up another table to figure out the pH at the half-equivalence point, or we could use a little common sense to avoid computation. At the half-equivalence point, half of the HN_3 has been consumed and converted to N_3^-. Therefore, the HN_3 and N_3 concentrations are equal.

$$K_a = \frac{[H_3O^+][N_3^-]}{[HN_3]} = [H_3O^+]$$

Because $[HN_3] = [N_3^-]$, $K_a = [H_3O^+]$, and $pH = pK_a = 4.72$.

Remember: Whenever possible, avoid computation!

3) Determine the reactive species at the equivalence point to find the pH.

At the equivalence point, all of the HN_3 has been consumed, leaving only N_3^- behind. Because N_3^- is a Brønsted-Lowry *base*, we need to worry about OH^-, not H_3O^+.

$$K_b = \frac{K_w}{K_a} = \frac{10^{-14}}{10^{-5}} = 10^{-9}$$

Remember that $K_a \times K_b = K_w = 10^{-14}$. Now we can set up our table:

	H_2O (l) + $N_3(aq)^-$ $\rightarrow$ HN_3 (aq) + $OH^-(aq)$		
Initial	—	0.15	0	0
Change	—	$-x$	$+x$	$+x$
Equilibrium	—	$0.15 - x$	x	x

Remember that the volume of our solution has increased by 40 mL, so the concentration of N_3^- is $\dfrac{0.02 \text{ mol}}{(0.1 + 0.04)\text{ L}} \approx 0.15$ *M*.

Make the approximation that $0.15 - x \approx 0.15$.

$$K_b = \frac{[HN_3][OH^-]}{[N_3^-]} = \frac{x^2}{0.15 - x} = \frac{x^2}{0.15} = 10^{-9}$$

Similar Questions

1) What is the pH after the equivalence point has been exceeded by 5 mL of the NaOH solution in the opening question?

2) What would be the pH if the same amount of NaOH solution necessary to get to the half-equivalence point in this titration were added to pure water? How does the pH of each situation compare? This demonstrates how weak acids can serve as *buffers*, solutions that resist changes in pH.

3) What would be the pH of a solution that was 0.2 *M* in HN_3 and 0.10 *M* in N_3^-?

Here, let's say that 1.6 is close to 1.5 to make the square root computation trivial.

$$x^2 = 0.15 \times 10^{-9} = 0.15 \times 10^{-10} \approx 1.6 \times 10^{-10} \approx 160 \times 10^{-12}$$
$$\Rightarrow x = \sqrt{160 \times 10^{-12}} = 4\sqrt{10} \times 10^{-6} \approx 12 \times 10^{-6} = 1.2 \times 10^{-5}$$
$$\Rightarrow [OH^-]_{eq} = 1.2 \times 10^{-5}$$
$$\Rightarrow pOH = -\log([OH^-]) = -\log(1.2 \times 10^{-5}) = 5 - \log(1.2) \approx 5$$
$$\Rightarrow pH = 14 - pOH = 14 - 5 = 9$$

Note that pH + pOH = 14 in water. Remember to ask yourself whether or not a result makes sense. Here, because we have a basic species (N_3^-), the pH should be above 7, which it is.

Key Concepts

Chapter 11

Oxidation

Reduction

Balancing electrochemical half-reactions

Balancing Redox Reactions

Balance the following reaction that takes place in basic solution.

$$ZrO(OH)_2(s) + SO_3^{2-}(aq) \rightleftharpoons Zr(s) + SO_4^{2-}(aq)$$

1) Separate the overall reaction into two half-reactions.

$$ZrO(OH)_2 \rightleftharpoons Zr$$
$$SO_3^{2-} \rightleftharpoons SO_4^{2-}$$

Break the reactions up by looking at atoms other than hydrogen and oxygen.

Takeaways

Don't fall into the trap of simply balancing mass in these reactions. If oxidation and reduction are occurring, you must go through this procedure to balance the reaction.

2) Balance the oxygens in each reaction by adding the necessary number of moles of water to the appropriate side.

$$ZrO(OH)_2 \rightleftharpoons Zr(s) + 3\ H_2O$$
$$H_2O + SO_3^{2-} \rightleftharpoons SO_4^{2-}$$

3) Balance hydrogen by adding the necessary number of H⁺ ions to the appropriate side of each reaction.

$$4\ H^+ + ZrO(OH)_2 \rightleftharpoons Zr + 3\ H_2O$$
$$H_2O + SO_3^{2-} \rightleftharpoons SO_4^{2-} + 2\ H^+$$

Things to Watch Out For

These kinds of problems can be extremely tedious. You must take extra care to avoid careless addition and subtraction errors!

4) If the reaction is carried out in basic solution, "neutralize" each equivalent of H⁺ with one equivalent of OH⁻.

$$4\ OH^- + 4\ H^+ + ZrO(OH)_2 \rightleftharpoons Zr + 3\ H_2O + 4\ OH^-$$
$$2\ OH^- + H_2O + SO_3^{2-} \rightleftharpoons SO_4^{2-} + 2\ H^+ + 2\ OH^-$$
$$4\ H_2O + ZrO(OH)_2 \rightleftharpoons Zr + 3\ H_2O + 4\ OH^-$$
$$2\ OH^- + H_2O + SO_3^{2-} \rightleftharpoons SO_4^{2-} + 2\ H_2O$$

Combine each mole of H⁺ and OH⁻ into one mole of water and simplify each reaction.

Remember: *Don't forget to add OH⁻ to each side of both reactions!*

5) Balance the overall charge in each reaction using electrons.

$$4\ e^- + 4\ H_2O + ZrO(OH)_2 \rightleftharpoons Zr + 3\ H_2O + 4\ OH^-$$
$$2\ OH^- + H_2O + SO_3^{2-} \rightleftharpoons SO_4^{2-} + 2\ H_2O + 2\ e^-$$

The top equation has a total charge of −4 on the right from the 4 moles of hydroxide, so 4 electrons need to be added to the left side of the equation.

In the bottom equation, there is a total charge of -4 on the left, -2 from the 2 moles of hydroxide, and -2 from the 2 moles of sulfite anion (SO_3^{2-}).

Remember: Don't forget to account for all charges in this step, including the charge contributed by molecules other than H^+ and OH^-.

---

6) Multiply each reaction by the necessary integer to ensure that equal numbers of electrons are present in each reaction.

$$4\ e^- + 4\ H_2O + ZrO(OH)_2 \rightleftharpoons Zr + 3\ H_2O + 4\ OH^-$$
$$4\ OH^- + 2\ H_2O + 2\ SO_3^{2-} \rightleftharpoons 2\ SO_4^{2-} + 4\ H_2O + 4\ e^-$$

Here, the lowest common multiple among the four electrons in the top reaction and the two in the bottom is four electrons, so we must multiply everything in the bottom reaction by two.

---

7) Combine both reactions and simplify by eliminating redundant molecules on each side of the reaction.

$$4\ e^- + 4\ H_2O(l) + ZrO(OH)_2(s) + 4\ OH^-(aq) + 2\ H_2O(l) + 2\ SO_3^{2-}(aq)$$
$$\rightleftharpoons Zr(s) + 3\ H_2O(l) + 4\ OH^-(aq) + 2\ SO_4^{2-}(aq) + 4\ H_2O(l) + 4\ e^-$$

Combine common terms on each side of the net reaction.

$$4\ e^- + 6\ H_2O(l) + ZrO(OH)_2(s) + 4\ OH^-(aq) + 2\ SO_3^{2-}(aq)$$
$$\rightleftharpoons Zr(s) + 7\ H_2O(l) + 4\ OH^-(aq) + 2\ SO_4^{2-}(aq) + 4\ e^-$$

Eliminate the redundant water molecules, as well as the electrons and excess hydroxide equivalents.

$$ZrO(OH)_2(s) + 2\ SO_3^{2-}(aq) \rightleftharpoons Zr(s) + 2\ SO_4^{2-}(aq) + H_2O(l)$$

Check to make sure that the reaction is balanced, in terms of both *mass* (number of atoms on each side) and *overall charge*.

*Remember: This last step is **extremely important.** If mass and charge aren't balanced, then you made an error in one of the previous steps.*

Similar Questions

1) Which atom is being oxidized in the original equation? Which is being reduced? Identify the oxidizing and reducing agents.

2) A *disproportionation* is a redox reaction in which the same species is both *oxidized* and *reduced* during the course of the reaction. One such reaction is shown below. Balance the reaction, assuming that it takes place in acidic solution:

$$PbSO_4(s) \rightarrow Pb(s) + PbO_2(s) + SO_4^{2-}(aq)$$

3) Dentists often use zinc amalgams to make temporary crowns for their patients. It is absolutely vital that they keep the zinc amalgam dry. Any exposure to water would cause pain to the patient and might even crack a tooth. The reaction of zinc metal with water is shown below:

$$Zn(s) + H_2O(l) \rightarrow Zn^{2+}(aq) + H_2(g)$$

Balance this reaction, assuming that it takes place in basic solution. Why would exposure to water cause the crown, and perhaps the tooth, to crack?

Key Concepts

Chapter 11

Oxidation/reduction

Electrochemical cells

Work

Stoichiometry

$E°_{cell} = E°_{cathode} - E°_{anode}$ (V)

$\Delta G° = -nFE°_{cell}$ (kJ/mol)

Electrochemical Cells

A galvanic cell is to be constructed using the $MnO_4^- \mid Mn^{2+}$ ($E°_{red}$ = 1.49 V) and $Zn^{2+} \mid Zn$ ($E°_{red}$ = −0.76 V) couples placed in an acidic solution. Assume that all potentials given are measured against the standard hydrogen electrode at 298 K and that all reagents are present in 1 M concentration (their standard states). What is the maximum possible work output of this cell per mole of reactant if it is used to run an electric motor for one hour at room temperature (298 K)? During this amount of time, how much Zn metal would be necessary to run the cell, given a current of 5 A?

1) Determine which half-reaction is occurring at the anode and which is occurring at the cathode of the cell.

$MnO_4^-(aq) + 5 e^- \rightarrow Mn^{2+}(aq)$ $E°_{red}$ = 1.49 V

$Zn^{2+}(aq) + 2 e^- \rightarrow Zn(s)$ $E°_{red}$ = −0.76 V

Compare the standard reduction potentials for both reactions. The permanganate reduction potential is greater than the zinc potential, so it would prefer to be reduced and zinc-oxidized. Therefore, the zinc is being oxidized at the anode and the manganese is being reduced at the cathode.

*Remember: **O**xidation occurs at the **a**node. (Hint: they both start with a vowel.)*

Takeaways

Double check your work when you balance the cell equation to make sure that you haven't made any arithmetic errors. One small addition or subtraction mistake can have drastic consequences!

2) Write a balanced reaction for the cell.

Balance the reactions one at a time.

$MnO_4^- \rightarrow Mn^{2+}$

Balance oxygen with water, and then hydrogen with acid (H⁺).

$8 H^+ + MnO_4^- \rightarrow Mn^{2+} + 4 H_2O$

Balance overall charge with electrons.

$8 H^+ + MnO_4^- + 5 e^- \rightarrow Mn^{2+} + 4 H_2O$

This one is easy; all you have to do is balance electrons.

$Zn \rightarrow Zn^{2+} + 2 e^-$

To combine both equations, we need to multiply each by the appropriate integer to get to the lowest common multiple of 2 and 5, which is 10.

$16 H^+ + 2 MnO_4^- + 10 e^- \rightarrow 2 Mn^{2+} + 8 H_2O$
$5 Zn \rightarrow 5 Zn^{2+} + 10 e^-$

Things to Watch Out For

Remember to balance the electron flow in order to figure out the maximum amount of work that the cell can perform.

Now add the equations up to get the balanced cell equation, and you're golden.

$$16 \, H^+(aq) + 2 \, MnO_4^-(aq) + 5 \, Zn(s) \rightarrow 2 \, Mn^{2+}(aq)$$
$$+ \, 5 \, Zn^{2+}(aq) + 8 \, H_2O(l)$$

3) Calculate the standard potential for the cell as a whole.

$$E°_{cell} = 1.49 \, V - (-0.76 \, V) = 2.25 \, V$$

Use the equation $E°_{cell} = E°_{cathode} - E°_{anode}$. Because the standard potential for the cell is positive, this confirms that this is a galvanic (or voltaic) cell—once you hook up the electrodes and immerse them in the designated solutions, current will start to flow on its own.

4) Compute $\Delta G°$ for the cell.

$$\Delta G° = -(10 \, mol \, e^-)(10^5 \, C \, mol^{-1})(2.25 \, V) = -2.25 \times 10^6 \, J \, mol^{-1}$$

$$\Rightarrow \text{maximum work output per mole of reactant} = 2.25 \times 10^3 \, KJ \, mol^{-1}$$

Use the equation $\Delta G° = -nFE°_{cell}$. The upper limit on the amount of work a reaction can perform is the same thing as $\Delta G°$.

Remember: *Power is work over time, and* $1 \, h = 3600 \, s \approx 4 \times 10^3 \, s$.

5) Use Faraday's constant to determine the number of moles of electrons transferred and to do any stoichiometric calculations.

$$4 \times 10^3 \, s \, (5 \, C \, s^{-1}) \, (10^{-5} \, mol \, e^- \, C^{-1}) = 0.2 \, mol \, e^-$$

Remember that current is charge passing though a point per unit of time, and Faraday's constant tells us how many coulombs of charge make up one mole of electrons.

$$0.2 \, mol \, e^- \left(\frac{1 \, mol \, Zn}{2 \, mol \, e^-} \right) = 0.1 \, mol \, Zn \times (70 \, g \, mol^{-1}) = 7 \, g \, Zn$$

The balanced half-reaction is used to determine the necessary mole ratio.

Similar Questions

1) How could you alter the cell setup to reverse the direction of current flow?

2) What would the cell potential be if Mn^{2+} and Zn^{2+} were at 2 *M* concentration and the MnO_4^- concentration remained at 1 *M*? Would changing the amount of zinc metal present in the cell change this potential? Why or why not?

3) Compute the minimum mass of potassium permanganate ($KMnO_4$) necessary to run the cell for the same amount of time as specified above.

The Nernst Equation

A galvanic cell is created at 298 K using the following net reaction:

$$2 H^+(aq) + Ca(s) \rightarrow Ca^{2+}(aq) + H_2(g)$$

Fluoride anions are added to the anode section of the cell only until precipitation is observed. Right at this point, the concentration of fluoride is 1.4×10^{-2} M, the pH is measured to be 0, the pressure of hydrogen gas is 1 atm, and the measured cell voltage is 2.96 V. Given this information, compute the K_{sp} of CaF_2 at 298 K.

Additional information:

$R = 8.314$ J (mol K)$^{-1}$

$Ca^{2+}(aq) + 2 e^- \rightarrow Ca(s)$ $E°_{red} = -2.76$ V

$2 H^+(aq) + 2 e^- \rightarrow H_2(g)$ $E°_{red} = 0.00$ V

$F = 96\ 485$ C mol^{-1}

1) Write down the expression for the K_{sp}.
The first part of this problem begins as with any other solubility problem: we need to write down the expression for the K_{sp}.

$$CaF_2(s) \rightarrow Ca^{2+}(aq) + 2 F^-(aq)$$

We're given the concentration of fluoride right when precipitation begins, so we can plug that right into the K_{sp} expression above. All we need is the concentration of Ca^{2+} ions, and we're golden.

$$K_{eq} = [Ca^{2+}][F^-]^2 = K_{sp}$$

2) Separate the net cell reaction into half reactions, and find $E°_{cell}$.

$Ca(s) \rightarrow Ca^{2+}(aq) + 2 e^-$ $E° = 2.76$ V
$2 H^+(aq) + 2 e^- \rightarrow H_{2(g)}$ $E° = 0.00$ V
NET: $2 H^+(aq) + Ca(s) \rightarrow Ca^{2+}(aq) + H_2(g)$
     $E°_{cell} = 0.00$ V $- (-2.76$ V$) = 2.76$ V

Now we know what the standard potential for the cell is. Our only problem is that, in the situation given in the problem, we are in *nonstandard conditions*, because the concentration of fluoride is not 1 M.

Remember: *Remember that $E°_{cell} = E°_{cathode} - E°_{anode}$.*

3) Apply the Nernst equation.

$$E = E° - \frac{RT}{nF} \ln Q$$

The reaction quotient (Q) in this case is of the cell reaction. Recall that the pressure of hydrogen gas is 1 atmosphere. As the pH = 0, $[H^+] = 10^{-0} = 1.0$ M.

$$Q = \frac{[Ca^{2+}]PH_{2(g)}}{[H^+]^2} = [Ca^{2+}]$$

$$E = E° - \frac{RT}{nF} \ln [Ca^{2+}]$$

$$E - E° = -\frac{RT}{nF} \ln [Ca^{2+}]$$

Rearrange the Nernst equation to solve for $\ln[Ca^{2+}]$.

$$-\left(\frac{nF}{RT}\right)(E - E°) = \ln [Ca^{2+}]$$

Start plugging in numbers. Here, $n = 2$ mol e$^-$, from the cell equation; $F = 96,485 \approx 100,000$ C mol^{-1}; T = 298 $\approx$ 300 K; R $\approx$ 8 J (mol K)$^{-1}$; and 2.96 − 2.76 = 0.2 = 2×10^{-1} V.

$$-\left(\frac{2 \times 10^5}{8 \times 300}\right)(2.96 - 2.76) = \ln [Ca^{2+}]$$

$$-\left(\frac{2 \times 10^5}{8 \times 300}\right)2 \times 10^{-1} = \ln [Ca^{2+}]$$

Here, assume $-16.7 \approx -20$.

$$-20 = \ln [Ca^{2+}]$$

$$-20 = 2.3 \log[Ca^{2+}]$$

Recall that $\ln x = 2.3 \log x$. Assume that $2.3 \approx 2.5$ so that $-\frac{20}{2.5} \approx -8$.

$$-8 = \log[Ca^{2+}]$$

$$[Ca^{2+}] = 10^{-8}$$

Similar Questions

1) If the K_{sp} of copper(I) bromide is 4.2×10^{-8}, compute the concentration of bromide necessary to cause precipitation in an electrochemical cell with the Cu|Cu$^+$ and H$^+$|H$_2$ couples. Assume the conditions are as follows: $E°_{red}$ of Cu$^+$ = 0.521 V; pH = 0; $P_{H2 (g)}$ = 1 atm; T = 298 K; E_{cell} when precipitation begins = 0.82 V.

2) Compute the equilibrium constant at 298 K for the cell comprised of the Zn^{2+} | Zn ($E_{red}°$ = −0.76 V) and MnO$_4^-$ | Mn^{2+} ($E_{red}°$ = 1.49 V) couples. Given this number, comment on the oxidizing ability of the permanganate anion.

3) A buffer solution is prepared that is 0.15 M in acetic acid and 0.05 M in sodium acetate. If oxidation is occuring at a platinum wire with 1 atm of H$_2$ bubbling over it that is submerged in the buffer solution, and the wire is connected to a standard Cu^{2+} | Cu half cell ($E_{red}°$ = 0.34 V), the measured cell voltage is 0.592 V. Based on this information, compute the pK_a of acetic acid.

Remember: When you absolutely must do computation, choose numbers that are easy to work with.

---

4) Plug the concentrations into the K_{sp} expression and solve.

$K_{sp} = [Ca^{2+}][F^-]^2$

$K_{sp} = (10^{-8})(10^{-2})^2 = 10^{-12}$

The "actual" value for the K_{sp} is 3.9×10^{-11}, so we are quite close.

Glossary

Absolute zero The temperature at which all substances have no thermal energy; 0K or −273.15°C.

Absorption spectrum The series of discrete lines at characteristic frequencies representing the energy required to make an electron in an atom jump from the ground state to an excited state.

Acid A species that donates hydrogen ions and/or accepts electrons. See **Acidic solution; Arrhenius acid; Brønsted-Lowry acid; Lewis acid.**

Acid dissociation constant (K_a) The equilibrium constant that measures the degree of dissociation for an acid under specific conditions. For an acid HA:

$$K_a = \frac{[H^+][A^-]}{HA}$$

Acidic solution An aqueous solution that contains more H^+ ions than OH^- ions. The pH of an acidic solution is less than 7.

Activated complex The transition state of a reaction in which old bonds are partially broken and new bonds are partially formed. The activated complex has a higher energy than the reactants or products of the reaction.

Activation energy (E_a) The minimum amount of energy required for a reaction to occur.

Adiabatic process A process that occurs without the transfer of heat to or from the system.

Alkali metals Elements found in Group IA of the periodic table. They are highly reactive, readily losing one valence electron to form ionic compounds with nonmetals.

Alkaline earth metals Elements found in Group IIA of the periodic table. Their chemistry is similar to that of the alkali metals, except that they have two valence electrons, and thus form 2^+ cations.

Amphiprotic species A reaction species that may either gain or lose a proton.

Amphoteric species A species capable of reacting as either on acid or base, depending on the nature of the reactants.

Anion An ionic species with a negative charge.

Anode The electrode at which oxidation occurs. Compare Cathode.

Antibonding orbital Molecular orbital formed by the overlap of two or more atomic orbitals whose energy is greater than the energy of the original atomic orbitals. See **Bonding orbital.**

Aqueous solution A solution in which water is the solvent.

Arrhenius acid A species that donates protons (H^+) in aqueous solution; e.g., HCl.

Arrhenius base A species that gives off hydroxide ions (OH^-) in aqueous solution; e.g., NaOH.

Atom The most elementary form of an element; it cannot be further broken down by chemical means.

Atomic mass The averaged mass of the atoms of an element, taking into account the relative abundance of the various isotopes in a naturally occurring substance. Also called the atomic weight.

Atomic mass units (amu) A unit of mass defined as $\frac{1}{12}$ the mass of a carbon-12 atom; approximately equal to the mass of one proton or one neutron.

Atomic number The number of protons in a given element.

Atomic orbital The square of the wavefunction of an electron. It describes the region of space where there is a high probability of finding the electron.

Atomic radius The radius of an atom. The average distance between a nucleus and the outermost electron. Usually measured as one-half the distance between two nuclei of an element in its elemental form.

Aufbau Principle The principle that electrons fill energy levels in a given atom in order of increasing energy, completely filling one sublevel before beginning to fill the next.

Avogadro's Number The number of atoms of molecules in one mole of a substance: 6.022×10^{23}.

Avogadro's Principle The law stating that under the same conditions of temperature and pressure, equal volumes of different gases will have the same number of molecules.

Azimuthal quantum number (l) The second quantum number, denoting the sublevel or subshell in which an electron can be found. Reveals the shape of the orbital. This quantum number represents the orbital angular momentum of the motion of the electron about a point in space.

Balanced equation An equation for a chemical reaction in which the number of atoms for each element in the reaction and the total charge are the same for the reactants and the products.

Balmer series Part of the emission spectrum for hydrogen, representing transitions of an electron between energy levels $n > 2$ to $n = 2$. These are four lines in the visible region of the spectrum.

Base A species that donates hydroxide ions or electrons, or that accepts protons. See **Arrhenius base; Basic solution; Brønsted-Lowry base; Lewis base.**

Base dissociation constant (K_b) The equilibrium constant that measures the degree of dissociation for a base under specific conditions. For a base BOH:

$$K_b = \frac{[B^+][OH^-]}{[BOH]}$$

Basic solution An aqueous solution that contains more OH^- ions than H^+ ions. The pH of a basic solution is greater than 7.

Body-centered cubic A crystalline unit cell described as a cube with one atom at each corner and an additional atom in the center (or body) of the cube.

Bohr model The model of the hydrogen atom postulating that atoms are composed of electrons that assume certain circular orbits about a positive nucleus.

Boiling point The temperature at which the vapor pressure of a liquid is equal to the surrounding pressure. The normal boiling point of any liquid is defined as its boiling point at a pressure of 1 atmosphere.

Boiling-point elevation The amount by which a given quantity of solute raises the boiling point of a liquid; a colligative property.

Bond energy The energy (enthalpy change) required to break a particular bond under given conditions.

Bonding orbital A molecular orbital formed by the overlap of two or more atomic orbitals whose energy is less than that of the original orbital. Compare Antibonding orbital.

Boyle's Law The law stating that at constant temperature, the volume of a gaseous sample is inversely proportional to its pressure.

Brønsted-Lowry acid Proton donor, e.g., H_3PO_4.

Brønsted-Lowry base Proton acceptor, e.g., OH^-.

Buffer A solution containing a weak acid and its salt (or a weak base and its salt) which tends to resist changes in pH.

Buffer region The region of a titration curve in which the concentration of a conjugate acid is approximately equal to that of the corresponding base. The pH remains relatively constant when small amounts of H^+ or OH^- are added because of the combination of these ions with the buffer species already in solution.

Calorie (cal) A unit of thermal energy (1 cal = 4.184 J).

Calorimeter An apparatus used to measure the heat absorbed or released by a reaction.

Catalysis Increasing a reaction rate by adding a substance (the catalyst) not permanently changed by the reaction. The catalyst lowers the activation energy.

Catalyst A substance that increases the rates of the forward and reverse directions of a specific reaction but is itself left unchanged.

Cathode The electrode at which reduction takes place.

Cation An ionic species with a positive charge.

Celsius (°C) A temperature scale defined by having 0°C equal to the freezing point of water and 100°C equal to the boiling point of water; also the units of that scale. Otherwise known as the centigrade temperature scale. 0 × C = 273.15K.

Charles' Law The law stating that the volume of a gaseous sample at constant pressure is directly proportional to its absolute (Kelvin) temperature.

Chemical bond The interaction between two atoms resulting from the overlap of electron orbitals, holding the two atoms together at a specific average distance from each other.

Chemical equation An expression used to describe the quantity and identity of the reactants and products of a reaction.

Chemical properties Those properties of a substance related to the chemical changes that it undergoes, such as ionization energy and electronegativity.

Closed system A system that can exchange energy but not matter with its surroundings.

Colligative properties Those properties of solutions that depend only on the number of solute particles present but not on the nature of those particles. See **Boiling-point elevation; Freezing-point depression; Vapor-pressure lowering.**

Common ion effect A shift in the equilibrium of a solution due to the addition of ions of a species already present in the reaction mixture.

Compound A pure substance that can be decomposed to produce elements, other compounds, or both.

Concentration The amount of solute per unit of solvent (denoted by square brackets), or the relative amount of one component in a mixture.

Conjugate acid-base pair Brønsted-Lowry acid and base reacted by the transfer of a proton, e.g., H_2CO_3 and HCO_3^-.

Coordinate covalent bond A covalent bond in which both electrons of the bonding pair are donated by only one of the bonded atoms. Also called a *dative bond*.

Covalent bond A chemical bond formed by the sharing of an electron pair between two atoms. See **Coordinate covalent bond; nonpolar covalent bond; polar covalent bond.**

Critical pressure The vapor pressure at the critical temperature of a given substance.

Critical temperature The highest temperature at which the liquid and vapor phases of a substance can coexist; above this temperature the substance does not liquefy at any pressure.

Crystal A solid whose atoms, ions, or molecules are arranged in a regular three-dimensional lattice structure.

***d* subshell** The subshells corresponding to the angular momentum quantum number $l = 2$, found in the third and higher principal energy levels; each containing five orbitals.

Dalton's Law The law stating that the sum of the partial pressures of the components of a gaseous mixture must equal the total pressure of the sample.

Daniell cell An electrochemical cell in which the anode is the site of Zn metal oxidation, and the cathode is the site of Cu^{2+} ion reduction.

Degenerate orbitals Orbitals that possess equal energy.

Delocalized orbitals Molecular orbitals whose electron density is spread over an entire molecule, or a portion thereof, rather than being localized between two atoms.

Density (ρ) A physical property of a substance, defined as the mass contained in a unit of volume.

Diamagnetic A condition that arises when a substance has no unpaired electrons and is slightly repelled by a magnetic field.

Diffusion The random motion of gas or solute particles across a concentration gradient, leading to uniform distribution of the gas or solute throughout the container.

Dipole A species containing bonds between elements of different electronegativities, resulting in an unequal distribution of charge in the species.

Dipole-dipole interaction The attractive force between two dipoles whose magnitude is dependent on both the dipole moments and the distance between the two species.

Dipole moment A vector quantity whose magnitude is dependent on the product of the charges and the distance between them. The direction of the moment is from the positive to the negative pole.

Disproportionation A redox reaction in which the same species acts as the oxidizing agent and as the reducing agent. For example:

$$Hg_2Cl_2 \rightarrow HgCl_2 + Hg$$

Dissociation The separation of a single species into two separate species; this term is usually used in reference to salts or weak acids or bases.

Electrochemical cell A cell within which a redox reaction takes place, containing two electrodes between which there is an electrical potential difference. See **electrolytic cell; voltaic cell.**

Electrode An electrical conductor through which an electric current enters or leaves a medium.

Electrolysis The process in which an electric current is passed though a solution, resulting in chemical changes that do not otherwise occur spontaneously.

Electrolyte A compound that ionizes in water.

Electrolytic cell An electrochemical cell that uses an external voltage source to drive a nonspontaneous redox reaction.

Electromagnetic radiation A wave composed of electric and magnetic fields oscillating perpendicular to each other and to the direction of propagation.

Electromagnetic spectrum The range of all possible frequencies or wavelengths of electromagnetic radiation.

Electromotive force (EMF) The potential difference developed between the cathode and the anode of an electrochemical cell.

Electron (e⁻) A subatomic particle that remains outside the nucleus and carries a single negative charge.

In most cases its mass is considered to be negligible ($\frac{1}{1,837}$ that of the proton).

Electron configuration The symbolic representation used to describe the electron occupancy of the various energy sublevels in a given atom.

Electronegativity A measure of the ability of an atom to attract the electrons in a bond. A common comparative electronegativity scale is the Pauling scale. Electronegativity is a periodic trend and a direct result of Z_{eff}.

Electron spin The intrinsic angular momentum of an electron, having arbitrary values of $+\frac{1}{2}$ and $-\frac{1}{2}$. See **Spin quantum number.**

Element A substance that cannot be further broken down by chemical means. All atoms of a given element have the same number of protons.

Emission spectrum A series of discrete lines at characteristic frequencies, each representing the energy emitted when electrons in an atom relax from an excited state to their ground state.

Empirical formula The simplest whole number ratio of the different elements in a compound.

Endothermic reaction A reaction which absorbs heat from the surroundings as the reaction proceeds (positive ΔH).

End point The point in a titration at which the indicator changes color, showing that enough reactant has been added to the solution to complete the reaction.

Enthalpy (H) The heat content of a system at constant pressure. The change in enthalpy (ΔH) in the course of a reaction is the difference between the enthalpies of the products and the reactants.

Entropy (S) A property related to the degree of disorder in a system. Highly ordered systems have low entropies. The change in entropy (ΔS) in the course of a reaction is the difference between the entropies of the products and the reactants.

Equilibrium The state of balance in which the forward and reverse reaction rates are equal. In a system at equilibrium, the concentrations of all species will remain constant over time unless there is a change in the reaction conditions. See **Le Châtelier's principle.**

Equilibrium constant (K_c or K_{eq}) The ratio of the concentration of the products to the concentration of the reactants for a certain reaction at equilibrium, all raised to their stoichiometric coefficients.

Equivalence point The point in a titration at which the number of equivalents of the species being added to the solution is equal to the number of equivalents of the species being titrated.

Excess reagent In a chemical reaction, any reagent whose amount does not limit the amount of product that can be formed. Compare **Limiting reagent.**

Excitation The promotion of an electron to a higher energy level by absorption of an energy quantum.

Excited state An electronic state having a higher energy than the ground state.

Exothermic reaction A reaction that gives off heat (negative ΔH) to the surroundings as the reaction proceeds.

f subshell The subshells corresponding to the angular momentum quantum number $l = 3$, found in the fourth and higher principal energy levels, each containing seven orbitals.

Face-centered cube A crystalline unit cell, cubic in shape, with atoms at each corner and at the center of each face.

Faraday (F) The total charge on 1 mole of electrons (1 F = 96,487 coulombs). Not to be confused with the farad (also denoted F), a unit of capacitance.

First law of thermodynamics The law stating that the total energy of a system and its surroundings remains constant.

Formal charge The conventional assignment of charges to individual atoms of a Lewis formula for a molecule, used to keep track of valence electrons. Defined as the total number of valence electrons in the free atom minus the total number of nonbonding electrons minus one-half the total number of bonding electrons. See **Lewis formula.**

Freezing point At a given pressure, the temperature at which the solid and liquid phases of a substance coexist in equilibrium.

Freezing-point depression Amount by which a given quantity of solute lowers the freezing point of a liquid. A colligative property.

Galvanic cell An electrochemical cell that uses a spontaneous redox reaction to do work, i.e., produce an electrical current. Also called a *Voltaic cell.*

Gas The physical state of matter possessing the most disorder, in which molecules interact only slightly; found at relatively low pressure and high temperatures. Also called vapor. See **Ideal gas.**

Gas constant (R) A proportionally constant that appears in the Ideal Gas Law equation, PV = nRT. Its value depends upon the units of pressure, temperature, and volume used in a given situation.

Gibbs free energy (G) The energy of a system available to do work. The change in Gibbs free energy, ΔG, can be determined for a given reaction from the equation $\Delta G = \Delta H - T\Delta S$. ΔG is used to predict the spontaneity of a reaction: a negative ΔG denotes a spontaneous reaction, while positive ΔG denotes a nonspontaneous reaction. See **Standard free energy.**

Graham's law The law stating that the rate of effusion of diffusion or a gas is inversely proportional to the square root of the gas's molecular weight.

Gram-equivalent weight The amount of a compound that contains 1 mole of reacting capacity when fully dissociated. One GEW equals the molecular weight divided by the reactive capacity per formula unit.

Group A vertical column of the periodic table, containing elements that are similar in their chemical properties.

Half-life The time required for the amount of a reactant to decrease to one-half of its former value.

Half-reaction Either the reduction half or oxidation half of a redox reaction. Each half-reaction occurs at one electrode of an electrochemical cell.

Halogens The active nonmetals in Group VIIA of the periodic table, which have high electronegativities and highly negative electron affinities.

Heat The energy representing the kinetic energy of molecules that is transferred spontaneously from a warmer sample to a cooler sample. See **Temperature.**

Heat of formation (ΔH_f) The heat absorbed or released during the formation of a pure substance from the elements at a constant pressure.

Heat of fusion (ΔH_{fus}) The ΔH for the conversion of 1 gram or 1 mole of a solid to a liquid at constant temperature and pressure.

Heat of sublimation (ΔH_{sub}) The ΔH for the conversion of 1 gram or 1 mole of a solid to a gas at constant temperature and pressure.

Heat of vaporization (ΔH_{vap}) The ΔH for the conversion of 1 gram or 1 mole of a liquid to a vapor at constant temperature and pressure.

Heisenberg uncertainty principle The principle that states that it is impossible to simultaneously determine with perfect accuracy both the momentum and position of a particle.

Henderson-Hasselbalch equation Approximate equation showing the relationship of the pH or pOH of a solution to the pK_a or pK_b and the ratio of the concentrations of the dissociated species.

Henry's Law The law stating that the mass of a gas that dissolves in a solution is directly proportional to the partial pressure of the gas above the solution.

Hess' Law The law stating that the energy change in an overall reaction is equal to the sum of the energy changes in the individual reactions which comprise it.

Heterogeneous Nonuniform in composition.

Homogeneous Uniform in composition.

Hund's Rule The rule that electrons will occupy all degenerate orbitals in a subshell with single electrons having parallel spins before entering half-filled orbitals.

Hybridization The combination of two or more atomic orbitals to form new orbitals whose properties are intermediate between those of the original orbitals.

Hydrogen bonding The strong attraction between a hydrogen atom bonded to a highly electronegative atom, (such as fluorine or oxygen) in one molecule, and a highly electronegative atom in another molecule.

Hydrolysis A reaction between water and a species in solution.

Hydronium ion The H_3O^+ ion in aqueous solution.

Hydroxide ion The OH^- ion.

Ideal gas A hypothetical gas whose behavior is described by the Ideal Gas law under all conditions. An ideal gas would have particles of zero volume that do not exhibit interactive forces.

Ideal Gas Law The law stating that $PV = nRT$, where R is the gas constant.

It can be used to describe the behavior of many real gases at moderate pressures and temperatures significantly above absolute zero. See **Kinetic molecular theory.**

Indicator, acid-base A substance used in low concentration during a titration that changes color over a certain pH range. The color change, which occurs as the indicator undergoes a dissociation reaction, is used to identify the end point of the titration reaction.

Inert gases The elements located in group 0 (or Group VIII) of the Periodic Table. They contain a full octet of valence electrons in their outermost shells; this electron configuration makes them the least reactive of the elements. Also called *Noble gases.*

Intermolecular forces The attractive and repulsive forces between molecules. See **van der Waals forces.**

Intramolecular forces The attractive forces between atoms within a single molecule.

Ion A charged atom or molecule that results from the loss or gain of electrons.

Ionic bonding A chemical bond formed through electrostatic interaction between positive and negative ions.

Ionic solid A solid consisting of positive and negative ions arranged into crystals that are made up of regularly repeated units and held together by ionic bonds.

Ionization product (IP) The general term for the dissociation of salts or of weak acids or bases; the ratio of the concentration of the ionic products to the concentration of the reactant for a reaction, all raised to their stoichiometric coefficients.

Ionization energy The energy required to remove an electron from the valence shell of a gaseous atom.

Isobaric process A process that occurs at constant pressure.

Isolated system System that can exchange neither matter nor energy with its surroundings.

Isothermal process Process that occurs at constant temperature in which the system either loses or gains heat in order to maintain that temperature.

Isotopes Atoms containing the same number of protons but different numbers of neutrons; e.g., nitrogen-14 and nitrogen-15.

Joule (J) A unit of energy; $1 \text{ J} = 1 \text{ kg m}^2/\text{s}^2$

Kelvin (K) A temperature scale with units equal to the units of the Celsius scale and absolute zero defined as 0 K; also the units of that temperature scale. Otherwise known as the absolute temperature scale. $0 \text{ K} = -273.15°C$.

Kinetic molecular theory The theory proposed to account for the observed behavior of gases. The theory considers gas molecules to be pointlike, volumeless particles exhibiting no intermolecular forces which are in constant random motion and undergo only completely elastic collisions with the container or other molecules. See **Ideal Gas Law.**

Law of conservation of mass The law stating that in a given reaction, the mass of the products is equal to the mass of the reactants.

Law of constant composition The law stating that the elements in a pure compound are found in specific weight ratios.

Le Châtelier's Principle The observation that when a system at equilibrium is disturbed or stressed, the system will react in such a way as to relieve the stress and restore equilibrium. See **Equilibrium.**

Lewis acid A species capable of accepting an electron pair; e.g., BF_3.

Lewis base A species capable of donating an electron pair; e.g., NH_3.

Lewis structure A method of representing the shared and unshared electrons of an atom, molecule, or ion. Also called a *Lewis Dot Diagram.*

Limiting reagent In a chemical reaction, the reactant present in such quantity as to limit the amount of product that can be formed.

Liquid The state of matter in which intermolecular attractions are intermediate between those in gases and in solids, distinguished from the gas phase in having a definite volume and from the solid phase in that the molecules may mix freely.

Lyman series A portion of the emission spectrum for hydrogen representing electronic transitions from energy levels n > 1 to $n = 1$.

Magnetic quantum number (m_ℓ) The third quantum number, defining the particular orbital of a subshell in which an electron resides. It conveys information about the orientation of the orbital in space.(e.g., p_x vs. p_y)

Mass A physical property representing the amount of matter in a given sample.

Mass number The total number of protons and neutrons in a nucleus.

Maxwell-Boltzmann distribution The distribution of the molecular speeds of gas particles at a given temperature.

Melting point The temperature at which the solid and liquid phases of a substance coexist in equilibrium.

Metal One of a class of elements located on the left side of the periodic table, possessing low ionization energies and electronegativities. Metals readily give up electrons to form cations; they possess relatively high electrical conductivity and are lustrous and malleable.

Metallic bonding The type of bonding in which the valence electrons of metal atoms are delocalized throughout the metallic lattice.

Metalloid An element possessing properties intermediate between those of a metal and those of a nonmetal. Also called a Semimetal.

Molality (m) A concentration unit equal to the number of moles of solute per kilogram of solvent.

Molarity (M) A concentration unit equal to the number of moles of solute per liter of solution.

Molar mass The mass in grams of 1 mole of an element or compound.

Mole (mol) One mole of a substance contains Avogadro's Number of molecules or atoms. The mass of 1 mole of substance in grams is the same as the mass of one molecule or atom in atomic mass units.

Mole fraction (X) A unit of concentration equal to the ratio of the number of moles of a particular component to the total number of moles for all species in the system.

Molecular formula A formula showing the actual number and identity of all atoms in each molecule of a compound.

Molecular orbital The region of electron density in chemical bonding that results from the overlap of two or more atomic orbitals. See **Bonding orbital; Antibonding orbital.**

Molecular weight The sum of the atomic weights of all the atoms in a molecule.

Molecule The smallest polyatomic unit of an element or compound that exists with distinct chemical and physical properties.

Monoprotic acid An acid that can donate only one proton, e.g., HNO_3. The molarity of a monoprotic acid solution is equal to its normality.

Nernst equation An equation that relates the voltage of an electrochemical cell to the concentrations of the reactant and products within that cell.

Net ionic equation A reaction equation showing only the species actually participating in the reaction.

Neutralization reaction A reaction between an acid and base in which H^+ ions and OH^- ions combine to produce water and a salt solution.

Neutral solution An aqueous solution in which the concentration of H^+ and OH^- ions are equal (pH = 7).

Neutron A subatomic particle contained within the nucleus of an atom. It carries no charge and has a mass very slightly larger than that of a proton.

Noble gases See **Inert gases.**

Nonelectrolyte A compound that does not ionize in water.

Nonmetal One of a class of elements with high ionization potentials and very negative electron affinities that generally gain electrons to form anions. Nonmetals are located on the upper right side of the periodic table.

Nonpolar bond A covalent bond between elements of the same electronegativity. There is no charge separation and the atoms do not carry any partially positive or partially negative charge. Compare **Polar bond.**

Nonpolar molecule A molecule which exhibits no net separation of charge, and therefore no net dipole moment.

Normality (N) A concentration unit equal to the number of gram equivalent weights of solute per liter of solution.

Nucleus The small central region of an atom; a dense, positively charged area containing protons and neutrons.

Octet Eight valence electrons in a subshell around a nucleus.

Octet rule A rule stating that bonded atoms tend to undergo reactions that will produce a complete octet of valence electrons. Applies without exception only to C, N, O, and F with zero or negative formal charges.

Open system A system that can exchange both energy and matter with its surroundings.

Orbital A region of electron density around an atom or molecule, containing no more than two electrons of opposite spin. See **Atomic orbital; Molecular orbital.**

Order of reaction In a calculation of the rate law for a reaction, the sum of the exponents to which the concentrations of reactants must be raised.

Osmosis The movement of a solvent or solute through a semipermeable membrane across its concentration gradient, i.e., from a container in which the concentration is high to a container in which the concentration is low.

Osmotic pressure The pressure that must be applied to a solution to prevent the passage of a pure solvent through a semipermeable membrane across its concentration gradient.

Oxidation A reaction involving the net loss of electrons or, equivalently, an increase in oxidation number.

Oxidation number The number assigned to an atom in an ion or molecule that denotes its real or hypothetical charge. Atoms, alone or in molecules, of standard state elements have oxidation numbers of zero. Also called the *oxidation state*.

Oxidizing agent In a redox reaction, a species that gains electrons and is thereby reduced.

p subshell The subshells corresponding to the angular momentum quantum number $l = 1$, found in the second and higher principal energy levels. Each subshell contains three dumbbell-shaped p orbitals oriented perpendicular to each other, and referred to as the p_x, p_y, and p_z orbitals.

Paired electrons Two electrons in the same orbital with assigned spins of $+\frac{1}{2}$ and $-\frac{1}{2}$. See **Orbital; Hund's rule.**

Paramagnetism A property of a substance that contains unpaired electrons: it is attracted by a magnetic field.

Partial pressure The pressure that one component of a gaseous mixture would exert if it were alone in the container.

Pathway The specific sequence of events bringing a system from one state to another.

Pauli exclusion principle The principle stating that no two electrons within an atom may have an identical set of all four quantum numbers.

Percent composition The percentage of the total formula weight of a compound attributed to a given element.

Percent yield The percentage of the theoretical product yield that is actually recovered when a chemical reaction occurs.

Period A horizontal row of the periodic table, containing elements with the same number of electron shells.

Periodic law The law stating that the chemical properties of an element depend on the atomic number of the elements and change in a periodic fashion.

Periodic table The table displaying all known chemical elements arranged in rows (periods) and columns (groups) according to their electronic structure.

pH A measure of the hydrogen ion content of an aqueous solution, defined to be equal to the negative log of the H^+ concentration.

Phase One of the three states of matter: solid, liquid, or gas.

Phase diagram A plot, usually of pressure versus temperature, showing which phases a compound will exhibit under any set of conditions.

Phase equilibrium For a particular substance, any temperature and pressure at which two or three phases coexist in equilibrium. See **Triple point.**

Photon A quantum of energy in the form of light with a value of Planck's constant multiplied by the frequency of the light.

Physical property A property of a substance related to its physical, not chemical, characteristics; e.g., density.

pOH A measure of the hydroxide (OH^-) ion content of an aqueous solution, defined to be equal to the negative log of the OH^- concentration.

Polar covalent bond A covalent bond between atoms with different electronegativities in which electron density is unevenly distributed, giving the bond positive and negative ends.

Polar molecule A molecule possessing one or more polar covalent bond(s) and a geometry that allows the bond dipole moments to add up to a net dipole moment, e.g., H_2O.

Polyprotic acid An acid capable of donating more than one proton, e.g., H_2CO_3.

Potential energy diagram An energy diagram that relates the potential energy of the reactants and products of a reaction to details of the reaction pathway. By convention, the x-axis shows the progression of the reaction, and the y-axis shows potential energy.

Precipitate An insoluble solid that separates from a solution, generally the result of mixing two or more solutions or of a temperature change.

Pressure Average force per unit area measured in atmospheres, torr (mm Hg), or Pascals (Pa). 1 atm = 760 torr = 760 mm Hg = 1.01×10^2 kPa.

Principal quantum number (n) The first quantum number, defining the energy level or shell occupied by an electron.

Proton (H^+) A subatomic particle that carries a single positive charge and has a mass defined as one or the hydrogen ion, H^+, which is simply a hydrogen nucleus, consisting of one proton. These species are considered to be equivalent.

Quantum number A number used to describe the energy levels available to electrons. The state of any electron is described by four quantum numbers. See **Principal quantum number; Azimuthal quantum number; Magnetic quantum number; Spin quantum number.**

Radioactivity A phenomenon exhibited by certain unstable isotopes in which they undergo spontaneous nuclear transformation via emission of one or more particle(s).

Raoult's law A law stating that the partial pressure of a component in a solution is proportional to the mole fraction of that component in the solution, i.e., $P_A = X_A P_{total}$.

Rate constant The proportionality constant in the rate law of a reaction; specific to a particular reaction under particular conditions.

Rate-determining step The slowest step of a reaction mechanism. The rate of this step limits the overall rate of the reaction.

Rate law A mathematical expression giving the rate of a reaction as a function of the concentrations of the reactants. The rate law of a given reaction must be determined experimentally.

Reaction intermediate A species that does not appear among the final products of a reaction but is present temporarily during the course of the reaction.

Reaction mechanism The series of steps that occur in the course of a chemical reaction, often including the formation and destruction of reaction intermediates.

Reaction rate The speed at which a substance is produced or consumed by a reaction.

Real gas A gas that exhibits deviations from the **Ideal Gas Law.**

Redox reaction A reaction combining reduction and oxidation processes. Also called *oxidation-reduction reaction*.

Reducing agent In a redox reaction, a species that loses electrons and is thereby oxidized.

Reduction A reaction involving the net gain of electrons or, equivalently, a decrease in oxidation number.

s **subshell** Subshell corresponding to the angular momentum quantum number $l = 0$, and containing one spherical orbital; found in all energy levels.

Salt An ionic substance, i.e., one consisting of anions and cations, but not hydrogen or hydroxide ions. Any salt can be formed by the reaction of the appropriate acid and base, e.g., KBr from HBr and KOH.

Saturated solution A solution containing the maximum amount of solute

that can be dissolved in a particular solvent at a particular temperature.

Second law of thermodynamics The law stating that all spontaneous processes lead to an increase in the entropy of the universe.

Semimetal See **Metalloid.**

Semipermeable A quality of a membrane allowing only some components of a solution, usually including the solvent, to pass through, while limiting the passage of other species.

Simple cubic structure A crystalline unit cell with atoms at each corner of a cube.

Solid The phase of matter possessing the greatest order, in which molecules are fixed in a rigid structure.

Solubility A measure of the amount of solute that can be dissolved in a solvent at a certain temperature.

Solubility product (K_{sp}) The equilibrium constant for the ionization reaction of a slightly soluble electrolyte.

Solute The component of a solution that is present in lesser amount than the solvent.

Solution A homogeneous mixture of two or more substances. It may be solid(e.g., brass), liquid(e.g., HCl(aq)), or gas(e.g., air).

Solvent The component of a solution present in the greatest amount;

the substance in which the solute is dissolved.

Specific Heat The amount of heat required to raise the temperature of one gram of a substance by 1°C.

Spectrum The characteristic wavelengths of electromagnetic radiation emitted or absorbed by an object, atom, or molecule.

Spin quantum number (m_s) The fourth quantum number, indicating the orientation of the intrinsic angular momentum of an electron in an atom. The spin quantum number can only assume values of $+\frac{1}{2}$ and $-\frac{1}{2}$.

Spontaneous process A process that will occur on its own without energy input from the surroundings.

Standard conditions Conditions defined as 25°C and 1 M concentration for each reactant in solution, and a partial pressure of 1 atm for each gaseous reactant. Used for measuring the standard Gibb's free energy, enthalpy, entropy, and cell EMF.

Standard free energy (G°) The Gibbs free energy for a reaction under standard conditions. See **Gibbs free energy.**

Standard hydrogen electrode(SHE) The electrode defined as having a potential of zero under standard conditions. All redox potentials are measured relative to the standard hydrogen electrode. The potentials are measured relative to the standard hydrogen electrode at 25°C and with 1.0 M of each ion in solution.

Standard potential The voltage associated with a half-reaction of a specific redox reaction. Generally tabulated as a reduction potential, compared to the SHE.

Standard temperature and pressure (STP) 0°C (273 K) and 1 atm. Used for measuring gas volume and density.

State The set of defined macroscopic properties of a system that must be specified in order to reproduce the system exactly. Sometimes also used as a synonym for *Phase*.

State function A function that depends on the state of a system but not on the path used to arrive at that state.

Strong acid An acid that undergoes complete dissociation in an aqueous solution; e.g., HCl.

Strong base A base that undergoes complete dissociation in an aqueous solution; e.g., KOH.

Sublimation A change of phase from solid to gas without passing through the liquid phase.

Subshell The division of electron shells or energy levels defined by a particular value of the azimuthal quantum number; e.g., *s, p, d,* and *f* subshells. Composed of orbitals. Also called Sublevels. See also **Orbitals.**

Surroundings All matter and energy in the universe not included in the particular system under consideration.

System The matter and energy under consideration.

Temperature A measure of the average energy of motion of the particles in a system.

Third law of thermodynamics The law stating that the entropy of a perfect crystal at absolute zero is zero.

Titrant A solution of known concentration that is slowly added to a solution containing an unknown amount of a second species to determine its concentration.

Titration, acid-base A method used to determine the concentration of an unknown solution.

Titration curve A plot of the pH of a solution versus the volume of acid or base added in an acid-base titration.

Torr A pressure unit equal to 1 mm Hg. 760 torr = 1 atm.

Transition metal Any of the elements in the B Groups of the periodic table, all of which have partially filled d sublevels.

Triple point The pressure and temperature at which the solid, liquid, and vapor phases of a particular substance coexist in equilibrium. See **Phase equilibrium.**

Unit cell A three-dimensional representation of the repeating units in a crystalline solid.

Unsaturated solution A solution into which more solute may be dissolved.

Valence electron An electron in the highest occupied energy level of an atom, whose tendency to be held or lost determines the chemical properties of the atom.

Van der Waals equation One of several real gas laws, or 'equations of state'. It corrects for attractive and repulsive forces assumed to be negligible in the ideal gas law.

Van der Waals forces The weak forces that contribute to intermolecular bonding, including hydrogen bonding, dipole-dipole interactions, and dispersion forces.

Vapor pressure The pressure exerted by a vapor when it is in equilibrium with the liquid or solid phase of the same substance. The partial pressure of the substance in the atmosphere above the liquid or solid.

Vapor-pressure lowering The decrease in the vapor pressure of a liquid caused by the presence of dissolved solute; a colligative property. See **Raoult's Law**

Voltaic cell See Galvanic cell.

Water dissociation constant (K_w) The equilibrium constant of the water dissociation reaction at a given temperature; 1.00×10^{-14} at 25.00°C.

Weak acid An acid that undergoes partial dissociation in an aqueous solution; e.g., CH_3COOH.

Weak base A base that undergoes partial dissociation in an aqueous solution; e.g., NH_4OH.

Yield The amount of product obtained from a reaction.

Z Nuclear charge. Equivalent to **atomic number.**

Z_{eff} Effective nuclear charge; the charge perceived by an electron form its orbital. Applies most often to valence electrons, and influences periodic properties such as **atomic radius** and **ionization energy.**

Index